New Directions in Teaching Secondary School Science

NEW TRENDS IN CURRICULUM AND INSTRUCTION SERIES
JOHN U. MICHAELIS, editor

New Directions in Teaching Secondary School Science

PAUL DEHART HURD
Professor of Education
Stanford University

RAND MCNALLY & COMPANY • CHICAGO

RAND McNALLY EDUCATION SERIES
B. OTHANEL SMITH, *Advisory Editor*

NEW TRENDS IN CURRICULUM AND INSTRUCTION SERIES
Edited by JOHN U. MICHAELIS

Evans and Walker, *New Trends in the Teaching of English in Secondary Schools*

Hurd, *New Directions in Teaching Secondary School Science*

Karplus and Thier, *A New Look at Elementary School Science*

Michaelis, ed., *Teaching Units in the Social Sciences*
  Vol. I, *Early Grades*
  Vol. II, *Grades III-IV*
  Vol. III, *Grades V-VI*

Scott, *Trends in Elementary School Mathematics*

Smith and Cox, *New Strategies and Curriculum in Social Studies*

Printed in U.S.A. by Rand McNally & Company
Library of Congress Catalogue Card Number 69:17209

Preface

Ten years ago a massive reform movement was generated to improve science teaching in America. New science courses were developed and tested in the schools. They not only contained new subject matter, but were written in terms of goals representing a new era in science teaching. These courses were designed to be taught differently and learned differently from the science courses of the past. It is these trends in curriculum development, instruction, and learning, along with their underlying philosophical and psychological assumptions, that are critically examined in this book.

At every grade level and for each science subject of the high school there are new alternative courses. These choices are described, their goals identified and their rationale explained. The chapter on evaluation trends provides criteria for making decisions about these new course offerings.

There is an extensive discussion on learning and the discipline-centered curriculum. How concepts are formed and how they may be taught are examined in terms of both the nature of science and the conditions for learning.

What has happened during the past decade to improve science teaching is the first phase in a long-range program of reform. These recent developments are a basis for recognizing trends and charting future directions. The second phase of the curriculum reform, the program for the *seventies,* will include more planning *for* trends rather than *from* trends. Today's science-based culture requires a curriculum unlike the past for reasons that are becoming increasingly more apparent. In the planning of this book the purpose has been to examine recent trends in secondary school science curriculum development and the perspective they provide for new directions.

PAUL DEHART HURD

1969
Stanford, California

Contents

I

The Demand for a Science Curriculum Reform

Modern America needs an education in the sciences that is up-to-date and relevant to contemporary life. The energetic efforts of the past decade to reform science teaching at the secondary school level have been in this direction. Hundreds of conferences have been held, millions of dollars invested and the talents of thousands of teachers, educators, scientists and laymen called upon to change the traditional science curriculum. Some groups sought to rethink and modify existing courses, while others spoke for more drastic action and for revolutionary changes. The latter groups proved to be the most influential with the result that new courses have been developed in biology, physics, chemistry, and earth science differing in purpose and content from the courses they are intended to replace.

A very logical question: What caused this massive curriculum movement to emerge, especially in science, where teachers were so certain about the accuracy of course content and so confident in the method of science? The question does not have a simple answer. The variety of forces influencing educational change is about as complex as the interactions found within an atom or a living cell. While some of the factors can be identified, the importance of each or just how they fit together is not always clear. Man's intellectual outlook changes, human values take on different meanings, and we become increasingly aware the world of today is no longer like that of yesterday. There is the wealth of new knowledge to consider as well as the new roles of science in society. At some point an awareness emerges:

the present curriculum is no longer serving the needs of either students or society.

Educational criticism usually arises from a loss of public confidence in the adequacy of existing programs. Typically in American history the concern about what is taught has followed a period of economic and social unrest. But in recent years, technological advancement and a knowledge explosion in science have fomented the doubts about what schools should be doing. Attention has been focused more on the content of subjects, its up-to-dateness and usefulness for modern living, and whether courses are being taught in an authentic or 'scientific' manner. These are the issues that lie at the heart of the current *discipline-centered* curriculum reform. The question not only concerns "what knowledge is of most worth," but what methods of instruction and learning are most efficient. The answers to these questions are being sought by carefully examining the structure of the scientific disciplines not only for improving the content of courses but for methods of teaching as well.

The task of updating science courses is more complicated than simply dropping out old material and adding the latest discoveries. Following the close of World War II, advances in science and technology increased at a tremendous rate. The advancement has been popularly described in stages—first as an *atomic age,* followed by an *age of automation,* then the *space age,* and currently the *computer age*—each symbolizing the new America and a new way of life. These changes were rapid, creating an increasing need for research specialists and for technical manpower. The first stimulus for science curriculum reform arose more out of a concern for manpower needs than it did for improving general education in the sciences. The emerging scientific-technological-industrialized society brought great demands for scientific manpower, not only in number but also in quality of training. At the same time it was increasingly apparent that the economic future of America was closely aligned with our ability to advance knowledge in the sciences and to find applications in technological innovations. National security was seen to rest more with increasing scientific intellectual resources than simply expanding the agricultural and industrial components of the United States. In this connection it is interesting to note that major financial support for the science curriculum reforms came from the National Defense Education Act and the National Science Foundation. As a people we seemed to have arrived at an appreciation of Alfred North Whitehead's statement of nearly a half century ago, "the race which does not value trained intelligence is doomed." It was also evident to attain this goal required something more than 'freshening up' the content of science courses.

The revolution in science and technology has touched nearly everyone in America. Automation has changed job patterns; newspapers and television feature achievements in space exploration and atomic developments; the results of medical research find a quick reception in large sections of the population; although the number of farmers in America has been declining, food production exceeds population demands and surpluses are common; and in a thousand other ways the average citizen is vaguely aware that 'science' has something to do with all this. He can talk about technical achievements such as computers, space probes, hybrid corn, jet planes, plastics, and detergents, but he is a stranger to the principles and theories of science underlying these developments. Even the few who know some basic scientific concepts rarely recognize them as intellectual achievements and as the product of human endeavor. The place of research in advancing science is unappreciated and is frequently restricted by a lack of public interest. One can only conclude the average American, through no real fault of his own, is scientifically and technologically illiterate. He confuses science with technology; he values the products of science more than scientific inquiry; he believes it is more worthwhile to know a few interesting facts about science than to understand its concepts and theories. At no point does he realize the history of modern science occupies the same span of time as the history of America, and that major contributions to the advancement of science originated with American scientists. To understand and appreciate the scientific enterprise, its contribution to western civilization and its place in the contemporary affairs of mankind, should be a major goal of pre-college science teaching—it is not. Young people graduating from high school are essentially foreigners in their own culture. The science curriculum with few exceptions has remained conservative in the midst of a scientific and technological revolution. It is conservative because it is more suited to an agrarian than a scientific-technological-industrialized society, and to a way of living that no longer exists. The demand is for a curriculum change in secondary school science to correct these educational ills, and to develop science courses more suitable for understanding the nature of the scientific enterprise and its meaning for modern America.

Implicit in the array of criticisms of science instruction was an expression of concern about the way science courses were being taught. Laboratory work was mostly a routine, and laboratory manuals were filled with blanks requiring 'right answers.' Although some advancements had been made in instructional resources, they were not widely used. Much teaching was a matter of either the teacher or students reciting the nomenclature and facts of science, and all too often it was the teacher. Learning was largely rote, supported by tests serving to inventory the student's current fund of information on the last chapter or two. In asking almost any adult whether he had science in high school, the likely answer was, "Yes, but don't ask me any questions since I have forgotten most of those names." This could hardly be called effective teaching. And again, to the average person, science has been something one studies in school, and not an essential part of education without which one lives in intellectual isolation from the modern world.

FORCES DIRECTING THE NEW SCIENCE CURRICULUM

The first pressure for curriculum reform was to obtain more and better scientific and technical manpower. This in turn focused attention on new programs for the gifted and the talented student. One panel composed of distinguished scientists, business leaders, university presidents and teachers assessed the problem in this way:

> The immediate implications for education may be briefly stated. We need an ample supply of high calibre scientists, mathematicians and engineers. Quantitative arguments over the shortages in these fields are beside the point. We need *quality* and we need it in considerable quantity! Whatever the existing needs, it is in the nature of a revolution that its continuing impetus derives from the unknown needs, the new opportunities and vistas which are the hallmark of creativity. We must develop guidance efforts designed to reach all able youngsters, and we must engage in a major expansion of the facilities for science teaching.[1]

The problem has been explored in more detail by John W. Gard-

[1] The "Rockefeller Report" on Education. *The Pursuit of Excellence*. Education and the Future of America. Garden City, New York: Doubleday and Company, Inc., 1958, p. 28.

ner and the issues have been placed in a broader educational and social context.[2]

The appeal for a better science education for the talented student was dramatic, the reasons seemed logical and schools responded with enthusiasm. There is little doubt but that for years the gifted and talented student was academically the most underprivileged in our high schools. Somehow he would take care of himself, and special programs for the scholarly had a low priority in curriculum development. Committees, commissions, the public press, and influential citizens commented fluently on the issue.[3] It took only a short period of time before the battle cry became: what is good for the gifted student is good for most students. Courses should be made more rigorous, frills reduced, and the school day and year lengthened. What the students got, however, were more courses, longer assignments, and more homework. Needless to say, these developments contributed very little toward improving the student's education in science. What was being sought was an education described as "excellent" or of a greater "quality." Neither of these terms was operationally defined, but they did indicate a new direction if one assumed the existing science curriculum did not have these characteristics.[4]

But there were other forces operating on the schools and not the least of these was the growing recognition that schools and colleges are an investment in knowledge and that the production of knowledge is a growing portion of our gross national product. Better education essentially means an improved economy.[5] For the past twenty-five

[2] Gardner, John W. *Excellence: Can We Be Equal and Excellent Too?* New York: Harper and Bros., 1961.

[3] For instance: Cole, Charles C., Jr. *Encouraging Scientific Talent.* New York: College Entrance Examination Board, 1956.

National Education Association. *The Identification and Education of the Academically Talented.* Washington, D.C.: NEA, 1958.

Rickover, H. G. *The Education of Our Talented Children.* New York: Thos. Alva Edison Foundation, Inc., 1957.

[4] See: Koerner, James D. (ed.). *The Case for Basic Education.* Boston: Little, Brown and Co., 1959; and Educational Policies Commission. *An Essay on Quality in Public Education.* Washington, D.C.: National Education Association, 1959.

[5] For a more detailed analysis of this point, the following books will be found helpful:

a. Harbison, Frederick and Myers, Charles E. *Education, Manpower and Economic Growth: Strategies of Human Resource Development.* New York: McGraw-Hill, 1964.

b. Machlup, Fritz. *The Production and Distribution of Knowledge in the United States.* Princeton, New Jersey: Princeton University Press, 1962.

years America has been moving more and more from a laboring to a learning society. Guidance workers are usually well supplied with charts and statistics to demonstrate to young people the value of an education in relation to financial earnings. And we have seen unemployment is greatest with those whose education is minimal. It is frequently pointed out a typical automated machine today has the equivalent of a high school education. In some subtle way the value of knowledge has permeated our society and in a decade college enrollments have doubled. In two states (California and Utah) the average level of education is some college (12.1 years), and while school drop-outs are a serious problem, we have never had a larger percentage of youth fourteen to seventeen years old in school than we have now. The demand for better schooling and the pressure to attend college are not unrelated problems and both forces have had an impact on the new science curriculum. The majority of the new nationwide science courses were developed for college preparatory students, especially the courses in chemistry and physics and to a lesser extent, the biology courses. At a later time a course in biology was developed for the 'slow learner.' It is quite evident we do not have science courses suitable for the range of student abilities and interests now found in secondary schools. It has been easier to exclude students from physics and chemistry than to develop courses which make it possible for all students to achieve some understanding of the physical world.

Efficiency has been a slogan of American business and industry for decades. It did not take long for those fomenting the present education reform to suggest that schools ought to be doing a more efficient job than they had been doing. Among the recommendations were: 1) better use of student time; 2) better textbooks; 3) better instruction; 4) more effective learning on the part of students; 5) better organization of science curriculum and less repetition; and 6) a rethinking of goals, such as, education for change rather than social adjustment. It was made clear that pupils need to learn more at every level of education than they did in the past and this is a possibility, but not with the traditional curriculum, school organization and teaching materials. Better sequenced courses, flexible scheduling, team teaching, simplified laboratory equipment, and single concept films represent a few of the current efforts to improve learning in the span of time available for teaching a course—the efficiency factor.

THE PROBLEM OF KNOWLEDGE

"The greatest threat to education—knowledge," was once the theme of a symposium held to celebrate the dedication of a new university science building. The amount of knowledge in every field of science is staggering and it is increasing at an accelerated rate. The time when it was possible to 'cover' a science in high school has long passed, and it appears equally improbable the major principles, laws, and theories of a discipline can be adequately taught in the 160–180 net clock hours available for a course. When we consider that the amount of knowledge doubles by the time children in the first grade reach high school, and that older science concepts—the atom and photosynthesis, for example—encompass more meaning each year, it is apparent curriculum innovations are needed to manage the knowledge problem.

There is also the problem of more things to know each year, for example, technological achievements which are inescapable in the life of each of us. We have seen the effects of automated production lines and computer monitored factories. Less well known is the use of computers to assist in classroom instruction and the identification of learning deficiencies; and in hospitals to help diagnose illness. Within a few years community computers will be available to housewives to help plan family diets, to budget expenses, to organize housekeeping chores, and to assist the children with their homework; pilot projects are well along. Almost any example of technological advance we might choose as an example of something new is likely to be a matter of historical record by the time this paragraph comes to your attention.[6]

The production of new knowledge in science and its applications in technology is changing our entire pattern of vocations and career advancement. There is an increasing percentage of jobs in the world requiring scientific or technical training. However, a major problem in career development is the fact it is no longer possible to prepare one for a lifelong career; the knowledge requirements change and many jobs become obsolete. This is not only a problem of those with

[6] Several encyclopedias have yearbooks on new developments in science and technology providing examples of what has happened during the past year.

a. *The World Book Science Annual.* Chicago: Field Enterprises Educational Corporation. Yearly editions.

b. *McGraw-Hill Yearbook of Science and Technology.* New York: McGraw-Hill. Yearly editions.

a limited education, but the Ph.D. in science can expect the significant knowledge in his field to change two or three times during his career. The majority of people are not likely to retire from the vocation with which they began their working life. We are all aware advancement in most vocational fields depends upon continually increasing one's knowledge; the need for mid-career retraining programs for scientists, teachers, doctors, and for most other occupations, is evident. We do not expect a science teacher, for example, to teach an acceptable course all his life on the basis of what he knew at graduation from college. These conditions suggest an education in science must prepare young people to learn on their own and expect to learn more after leaving school than they did in school. This is one reason for the emphasis in education today on 'learning to learn,' upon 'inquiry,' and 'discovery' techniques.[7] We must enable students to undertake later career changes and be flexible enough to meet them successfully.[8]

Since the generation of knowledge is a major endeavor in our society, we must find ways of solving the problems created by the production of new knowledge. This is not an unreasonable demand on education, it simply means the science curriculum commonly used in the past is not adequate. The curriculum was quite uniform from school to school—essentially a national curriculum although unofficial; in nearly all chemistry courses the physical properties of selected elements were recited, and from course to course the elements were usually the same ones. It was a rare biology teacher who did not have students learn the parts of a root, stem, flower, fruit and seed once for the monocotyledons and again for a dicotyledon, and the objective was to know the parts—sometimes there was a bonus for correct spelling on the test. Levers and sound were sure to be taught in physics courses primarily for the reason that other physics teachers were not leaving these topics out. All of these topics were taught in science courses before 1900 and they comprise the questions on final examination papers a half century

[7] For a background discussion of this problem see: Bruner, Jerome (ed.). *Learning About Learning: A Conference Report.* OE–12019. Cooperative Research Monograph No. 15. Washington: U.S. Office of Education, Government Printing Office, 1966.

[8] The problems of vocational education are described in: Barlow, Melvin L. (ed.). *Vocational Education.* The Sixty-fourth Yearbook of the National Society for the Study of Education, Part I. Chicago: University of Chicago Press, 1965.

later. And along with many other topics in biology, physics, and chemistry they have been emphasized as basic, but if examined in terms of progress within the related discipline they will be seen as more traditional than basic. The question is not so much whether these topics should be taught but whether they are of the greatest value in terms of what is now known for interpreting the natural world and meeting the problems of the future.[9]

However we look at modern society and advances in science and technology it becomes apparent an education for an era of rapid change must be different in character from any of the past. It is not that the traditional goals for science teaching were in error, but they were for an age no longer in existence. Young people should be educated for the world in which they will be living and the purposes for teaching science need to be defined in these terms.[10]

Since the natural sciences are distinguished by a continual flow of new knowledge, by refinements of existing knowledge, accompanied by new theories and models, the teaching of science must reflect these same dynamic characteristics. There needs to be a curriculum program to prevent courses from becoming essentially a dogma based upon tradition. This is inconsistent with the nature of science and, as such, provided a major stimulus for the present reform in science teaching. Several means for improving the situation as reflected in the new curricula are: 1) placing a greater emphasis upon rational thinking as a course outcome; 2) using the discipline as a criterion for the selection of instructional materials; 3) organizing the curriculum with both a concept and inquiry sequence; and 4) shifting more responsibility for learning to the student. These points will be discussed in some detail in later chapters.

[9] For a detailed discussion on the teaching of biology and earlier attempts to reform the curriculum see: Hurd, Paul DeHart. *Biological Education in American Secondary Schools 1890–1960*. Washington, D.C.: American Institute of Biological Sciences, 1961.

[10] These references describe something of the social and cultural changes having implications for the teaching of science:

a. Journal of the American Academy of Arts and Sciences. *DAEDALUS*. "Science and Culture" (entire issue). Winter, 1965.

b. Meier, Richard L. *Science and Economic Development: New Patterns of Living*. New York: John Wiley and Sons, 1956.

For a more general statement of the problem and its meaning for science education, the following reference contains a wide range of viewpoints: Elbers, Gerald W. and Duncan, Paul (eds.). *The Scientific Revolution: Challenge and Promise*. Washington, D.C.: Public Affairs Press, 1959.

SCIENCE EDUCATION FOR AN ERA OF RAPID CHANGE

We are living in a new world, a period of rapid change and progress, and it is getting newer every day. The task in science teaching is to provide young people with the kind of education which will not only provide an understanding of today's problems but help to recognize and interpret signals for the future. In science there is more new knowledge than old, an imbalance not evident in other teaching fields. Much new knowledge represents a break with the past, and whether the new is true remains for the future to demonstrate. These are among the observations bringing the traditional science curriculum into disrepute. The question now is one of how to design a curriculum and develop the intellectual skills and attitudes essential for progress within a system of continuous change. Essentially the task is one of providing an education which makes it possible for youth to understand today's world and at the same time be prepared to meet the unknown problems of tomorrow—ten, twenty or thirty years from now. If we are not able to do this we will always be educating youth for a world that no longer is. This is why there is so much criticism of science courses with a fixed body of content, learned in a rote manner, and out of context with the inquiry processes generating the knowledge. In these courses the mind of the student is treated as a storehouse to be filled with information, in contrast to being viewed as an instrument for thinking.

The sciences are particularly suited for an education built upon reasoning, problem solving, and change. In actuality, it is only within a framework of evolving concepts, probabilities and investigation that science can be learned in an honest fashion. Science in a sense is a future-oriented discipline; it grows upon the revision and cumulation of knowledge; there is always the effort to refine old ideas, to improve models and theories—"science, the endless frontier." What has been achieved in the past is only a prologue to the future. But much of science teaching is based upon the assumption tomorrow will not be much different from today. This point of view is inconsistent with the realities of contemporary society and it never has been true of science. A modern curriculum in science must of necessity be one that enables young people to have access to new knowledge, to expect change, and to behave rationally and creatively toward the problems generated by change; to better insure change will mean progress.

We must also recognize that advancement in society, like progress in science, creates as many problems as it solves; the new problems are of a different sort and require previously untried methods for solution. The present is something more than simply an extension of the past, if for no other reason than scientific knowledge becomes more complex, as do social developments. This means a total reassessment of the curriculum and the restructuring of a school program in harmony with the complexities of a modern scientific-technological-industrialized society. It seems reasonable to expect the emerging science curriculum to have few characteristics in common with the past. We need new goals for a new kind of education for a new world. The most we know about this future world is it will be different, complex, and dynamic and individuals will have responsibilities for which they have not had specific training. But at the same time they will be expected to act creatively in fostering change and innovation.

Within this chapter we have sought to establish a perspective for the present curriculum reform movement in science teaching. We shall see in later chapters an expansion of some of these ideas and the introduction of others. Within this matrix of social and scientific forces the new science curriculum developments will be examined and the new trends and directions identified both in rationale and practice.

II

The Nature of Science and Science Curriculum Reform

THE PROBLEM IN PERSPECTIVE

Science curricula are not permanent nor should they necessarily have a long life. They are constantly disrupted by a changing society, by their own inadequacies, and by new developments within the disciplines they represent. We examined some of these conditions in the previous chapter, particularly the changing social scene in America. Looking back to 1900 we found the unsanitary and poor health conditions of that time giving rise to a civic biology, a course oriented toward improving these conditions. Later (c. 1915), because of the growing industrialization of America, it seemed important to include in chemistry courses processes such as making steel, mining sulfur, manufacturing sulfuric acid, and smelting ores. Concurrently, the growing use of telephones, internal combustion engines, wireless telegraphy, electrical appliances, and airplanes caused these topics to be included in physics courses. General science, a new course at this time, was developed to serve as an introduction to biology, physics and chemistry and to whet the curiosity of students with the technological marvels of the time. The depression years of the 1930's led to courses called "consumer science." Their major goal was to use the knowledge of science to provide a base for the intelligent purchase of goods and services. The war years of the 1940's saw 'air-age' biology, physics and chemistry come into being and quickly fade away. The technical manpower crisis of the 1950's prompted numerous programs designed for the gifted student in science. In the 1960's, problems of integration, of poverty pockets, and of urban schools created a demand for a science curriculum suited to the 'disadvantaged' or the 'slow learner.' Each major social crisis in American life tends to be reflected in the science program by changes in curriculum content, in goals to be sought, in the organization of courses, and in the modes of teaching. Some of the new approaches resulted from careful deliberations by teachers and educators, while others were forced upon the school by critics and public pressures; less frequently they reflected the results of educational research and changes in learning theory.

When we examine the science curriculum reform of this decade we find most of the pressures for change came from scientists. They raised the significant question, are the high school science courses in fact truly representative of science, especially as science is known to scientists? One scientist described the situation this way: "high school teachers are so busy teaching biology, chemistry and physics they forget to teach the science of their subjects." The teachers' reaction was, we are teaching what we were taught and in our pre-service education very little time, if any, was devoted to "learning about science as science."

Practically no one was of the opinion the pre-1960 science courses were the very best that could be devised. But there has never been an effective mechanism for developing new curricula. The practice has been to repair curriculum breakdowns by correcting the isolated defects. This means updating the content, correcting errors, changing the order of topics, rewriting to clarify meaning, substituting a new laboratory exercise that might work better, and doing whatever patchwork seems necessary. Rarely is this work done with the guidance of an educational theory to provide a rationale for changes, or in the light of psychological assumptions to improve pupil learning.

The public temper of the 1950's was one of rejecting the high school program for science teaching. It was an across-the-board faultfinding, including curriculum, methods of teaching, and education of teachers. No serious attempt was made to distinguish between good and bad educational practices or effective and ineffective teachers. No one seemed to remember that in the last half century the American schools were primarily responsible for bringing a common language to tens of millions of immigrants and a commitment to a concept of democracy as a way of life, a feat no other country has accomplished in so short a period of time with so many people. Few remembered that in this same span of time America became, mostly because of widespread education, the world's greatest scientific-technological-industrialized society. One should add this happened despite the pressures of two World Wars, a ten-year economic depression, and two revolutions—one in technology and one in science. But public opinion was to the effect science education was not doing the job it should *now* be doing; the curriculum was seen as out-of-date and out-of-step with society.

Critics of the schools whose training was in science became the educational philosophers for the new curricula. The public for the most part trusted their statements whether they were rational or irrational, and there were some of each. To be sure, the science curriculum was very much a patchwork, poorly organized, and out-of-date; but only the irrational critics could propose a solution recommending American schools adopt a Soviet science program or "go back to the basics," which usually turned out to be course content and educational practices found inadequate decades to centuries ago. Fortunately more sober views on the problem dominated and the decision was made to debate the issue in the Congress of the United States.[1]

A NEW EDUCATION PHILOSOPHER EMERGES

The crisis in science teaching reached a climax in the middle of the 1950's and a curriculum *reform* was sought, something more drastic than the minor revisions characteristic of past efforts. The question raised was who is most worthy to restructure pre-college education in the sciences? The National Science Foundation, which had been asked by the Congress of the United States to make the decision, chose the professional scientist as the most qualified person to improve high school science courses. For example, the research physicist is the person who knows physics best and is therefore the one to revitalize the physics courses; the same rationale was used to select directors for writing 'new' biology, chemistry, and earth science

[1] Eighty-Fifth Congress, Second Session. *Hearings Before the Committee on Labor and Public Welfare, United States Senate on Science and Education for National Defense.* Washington, D.C.: Government Printing Office, 1958, (1,602 pages).

courses. The assumption was implicitly made that high school science teachers, professional educators, and textbook writers had failed to propose a modern concept of science education and were not able to devise a curriculum appropriate to understanding modern science. Under these conditions the only recourse was to appoint new leadership: the natural scientist. Typically he is an active researcher, closely identified with the professional scientific societies, and has published widely enough to have his name recognized by people in science generally and by the informed public. At one time or another he has written articles, given talks, or otherwise made known his concerns about the teaching of science. These qualifications mean that he can, if properly financed, attract the interest of his peers in a curriculum effort and his established position in the scientific community will lend authenticity to his curriculum efforts.

The new science education philosopher is not a generalist as are most educational theorists. Rather he is a person who understands biology, or chemistry, or physics, or is an expert on one of the earth sciences. Since his competence is that of a specialist he seeks only to improve the high school course matching his research interests. This is one of the reasons the current curriculum reform movement has been labeled a "discipline-centered approach." As specialists the project directors did not concern themselves with the development of a coordinated science curriculum for high schools. Any results in this direction, and there are some, may only be regarded as fortuitous.

THE SCIENTIST STATES HIS CURRICULUM RATIONALE

The teaching of science in high school should reflect the nature of science as it is known to scientists. While there are commonalities between various sciences, the teaching of any particular course should first of all embody the specific characteristics of the discipline it represents. For example, the concepts and methods of high school physics should reflect the theories and thinking of modern physics. In biology, chemistry, and the earth sciences the same kind of relationship between the discipline and the corresponding high school course should exist.

One characteristic of a discipline is the conceptual structure identifying the knowledge of which it is composed. Disciplines also have particular modes of inquiry, a special way of gathering information and processing it into data. These inquiry processes are not exactly the same for all sciences. Biologists do not inquire into problems and interpret observations in the same vein as chemists, and both differ from anthropologists in their procedures. Whatever the methods of inquiry they are *disciplined* procedures and there are 'ground rules' governing these processes. Actually there is no one method that characterizes science, but rather there are guidelines which map the pathways to understanding.

The scientist's point of view on curriculum development is quite clear: a high school course should be a mirror image of a science discipline, with regard to both its conceptual structure and its patterns of inquiry. The theories and methods of modern science should be reflected in the classroom. In teaching a science, classroom operations should be in harmony with its investigatory processes and supportive of the conceptual, the intuitive, and the theoretical structure of its knowledge. The opinion of the curriculum reformers was that not one published textbook or course of study in high school science met these requirements. The only recourse was to start from the beginning and write new science textbooks consistent with the philosophical assumptions of what an authentic course in high school science should be.

THE NATURE OF SCIENCE

To fully appreciate the science curriculum reform movement and the trends in science teaching one needs a clear notion of what is meant by science. This is important because a major criticism of traditional high school science courses is they are weak in their science content and do not provide the student with a valid understanding of what is meant by science. It is undoubtedly true, a teacher's concept of what science is influences not only what he teaches but how he teaches. It would simplify things if a clear-cut description of science were available—one which most scientists would agree to—but it is not. Science is a complex of intellectual activities and human purposes that defies definition with one or a few sentences.

In the modern sense, science began when men thought of it as a method by which the natural world could be explored and known with greater reliability than it had been in the past. About 400 years ago men recognized the value of systematic observation, measurement, and experimentation as the means for developing scientific knowledge. In this sense science is a method for studying the natural world, but in no sense is this method a uniform or precise set of procedures or rules. The methodology of science cannot be formalized apart from either the scientist as a person or the problem upon which he is working. No one procedure is any more effective in leading to discoveries than another; science is more an outcome of one's thinking than it is of the research procedures he uses.

In the public mind and in school practice science is frequently identified as a method for solving problems. A situation exists in which there is an identifiable problem; relevant known facts are assembled; these are organized into a hypothesis; the hypothesis suggests the requirements for additional information and experimentation, which in turn may lead to the solution of the problem. This is the way, for example, one goes about improving crops, making better computers, and solving the problems of space travel. In traditional science courses these are the 'steps' in an experiment. This is not, however, the way in which science works. While it is the experiment which typically distinguishes modern science from its forerunners, it is, as Karl R. Popper has pointed out, "the theory and not the experiment, which opens up the way to new knowledge." At the same time it is important to recognize that experimentation and theory are interdependent, each nourishing the other. The scientist who experiments—and not all do—is always something of a theorist, otherwise there is no way for him to interpret his observations. Not all experiments are carried out in the laboratory; many are mental experiments in which the experimenter examines an idea by asking himself questions and exploring for insight in terms of data, laws, and theories with which he is already knowledgeable.

Observations and experiments supply scientists with an endless array of facts. But the accumulation of information on a topic does not provide an interpretation. The scientist tries to bring order to relevant facts. It is always necessary to make facts and observations into data before they become useful either to answer questions or to form the basis for new questions. The questioning process is an endless one, since one is never quite certain the most useful question has been asked.

Science is a continuing process of seeking new knowledge, new explanations, and deeper understanding. New discoveries tend to generate new questions which call for further observations and more experimentation. The data abstracted from observations must at some point be fitted into a model, theory, or law to become meaningful. To understand science we must have some idea of how data are formed, where they fit into the conceptual structure of science, and what the limitations upon their explanatory status are. To appreciate science requires much more than a fund of scientific information. Facts and individual observations in science are meaningless by themselves. Alone they are, as Whitehead described them, "inert." Their usefulness arises as we try to fit them into a logical order. At times facts are stubborn and resist becoming a part of the way our ideas are now organized. This means either the conceptual model to which the new fact is relevant must be modified, or a new model needs to be thought through. Facts in and of themselves do not make a science. A science is not simply an abstraction from empirical data, but an intellectual creation often suggested by the data. It is the discovery of order among the data that makes the science, and this process requires a constructive imagination, intuition, and an intellectual command of relevant concepts. This is why being well informed about science is not the same as knowing science; science is an intellectual activity which arises from personal experience and takes place in the minds of men. It is simply a way of using human intelligence to achieve a better understanding of nature and nature's laws. But, as we shall note in detail later, this is not the spirit in which conventional science courses have been taught: this is what disturbed the curriculum reformers.

UNCERTAINTY IN SCIENCE

The science we read in texts, assuming the book is up-to-date, represents only the current status of scientific knowledge. Seldom is it emphasized that ideas are developed over a long period of time and what is known today is only a phase in the evolution of a concept. It is for philosophers to debate whether in time we will know the ultimate truth. For all practical purposes we are on safer ground if we assume every scientific statement is tentative forever. The process of science is such that its knowledge is under constant revision and refinement; no fact, concept, law or theory of science is incorrigible.

Or, to put the matter another way, scientific knowledge is cumulative, and the notion of completeness is not a part of the enterprise. The laws and theories of science are probabilities and present insights always limit the extent to which they are predictive. Much of the activity of the scientists is to keep the situation just this way.

One problem in science teaching occurs because the subject is frequently taught as dogma. The imperfections of knowledge are seldom pointed out, rather an impression of finality and 'truth' is conveyed. Students leave courses not only thinking they now have the answers, but what is worse, feeling it must have been fun in the good old days when there were still opportunities to make discoveries in nature. They are not made aware there may be several acceptable explanations for an observation and the choice is open to select the one most useful or satisfying at the moment. In science good answers to questions are most likely those illuminated by a theory, but there are no 'right' answers.

The mode of teaching high school science courses keeps the revisionary character of science essentially a secret. Few lessons are planned to illustrate science as a dynamically changing system of concepts and theories. This would require a consideration of the beliefs and contradictions of yesterday, and a recognition of unsolved problems and speculations about the future.

CONTROVERSY IN SCIENCE

How science and its attributes are interpreted by different scientists and at different times in history should be noted. These characteristics and the identifiable causes are fields of study for the historian and philosopher of science. In the long run, however, the evolutionary character of science has obvious implications for the curriculum and at critical times influences educational decisions. We are in such a period now and it raises these questions: should we be teaching classical physics (Newtonian mechanics) or modern physics? natural history or molecular biology? This is not simply a matter of choosing different subject matter, but represents a difference in the way of thinking about physics and biology.

There are other kinds of debates about the scientific enterprise: Are new ideas in science a product of invention or discovery? Is the purpose of the experiment to confirm or refute the hypothesis? Do hypotheses define the data or are hypotheses invented from data? Do diverse contexts 'prove' the hypothesis or are there many criteria for judging the worthiness of a hypothesis? Answers to these questions reflect a point of view about science and an interpretation of its ethos—the responses are not uniform. Whatever the response it has implications for the content of the curriculum, the purpose of experiments, and the way science is explained to young people.

SCIENCE AND TECHNOLOGY

The distinction between science and technology is a major issue in the current science curriculum reform. The identification of science with technology is a product of this century and, in the public mind and in the teaching of science, is a matter of much misinterpretation. Scientists feel the traditional science courses place too much emphasis on technological achievements and industrial uses of science. They criticize the failure of teachers to distinguish clearly enough the differences between scientific achievements and technological advances, the interactions between them, and their separate contributions. The relationship between science and technology is an evolving one and the kind of interdependence we find today is not like that existing earlier in this century or the conditions giving rise to the industrial revolution of 1760.

It is not my intention to debate the question of science and technology in the curriculum, but to distinguish between them sufficiently to illustrate the arguments of the scientist for a discipline-centered curriculum in high school. Science, as we have seen, is a process of thinking, a means of acquiring new knowledge, and a means of understanding the natural world. Technology is much more ancient than science. The original definition of technology is "the systematic knowledge of the industrial arts." The working of stone to make arrowheads, potterymaking, weaving, and the casting of metals are early examples of technology. None of these activities were based on a knowledge of science. In the period from 1500 to 1700 the first efforts to apply science to technology appeared—that is, using the knowledge of science to control or modify nature. Within the last 100 years more men have become active in applying science than in adding to its basic knowledge. Berkner states, "the crossover from empirical to science-based technologies occurred about the mid-century." He estimates that by the year 2000 "technology will have become almost completely science based, deriving its strength from the constructs and basic generalizations of science."[2]

Scientists are interested in seeking knowledge for its own sake because it may help to better describe or understand human experience. The technologists, though their education may be that of scientists, are primarily interested in the practical uses of scientific information. They may engage in research but it is directed to a specific end or to the solution of a particular problem, getting men on the moon for example. This is a very complex series of problems, including not only how to get to the moon but how life can survive. In many ways the known laws and principles of science define the problems, but it is up to the technical expert to solve them. This kind of problem solving activity has been the one most frequently identified as a major goal of teaching in conventional science courses. It is in contrast to 'science as inquiry' in the new curriculum.

Not only is science confused with technology, but technology is frequently interpreted as technique and technicians as technologists. Discoveries are credited to technicians, when what is meant is either technologists or scientists. Usually a scientist is a good technician, but a good technician is not necessarily a scientist. Scientists are primarily concerned with thinking: technicians are experts in the use of tools; but both scientists and technicians are essential to technological progress. Science is an explanatory and interpretive activity, a creative enterprise; the technicians' performances are those of craftsmen or artisans. Although both scientists and technicians are essential to scientific progress, the problem is to teach science in its proper image.

Space probes, computers, automated machines, manmade satellites, tranquilizers, and plastics are technological achievements. They get considerable attention in newspapers and magazine articles; periods in civilization are named after them—space age, atomic age, age of automation, computer age—but for all of this, they represent only the 'current events' of technology and, indirectly, a happening in science. It is no more possible to teach science from its current events than it is to teach history from current events. The educational question involves the proper place of science and technology in high school science courses. In the curriculum reform movement the de-

[2] Berkner, L. V., *The Scientific Age: The Impact of Science on Technology*. New Haven: Yale University Press, 1964.

cision was to place all the emphasis upon science. None of the new science curricula list understanding technology or its relation to science as a goal.

How scientists view the relationship of science and technology is interesting. Heisenberg regarded technology as a starting point and a consequence of science. Louis Pasteur said it this way: "There is science and the application of science, bound together as the fruit to the tree which bears it." And James B. Conant compared the relationship to a "wide continuous spectrum." Eric M. Rogers in his essay on the aims of science teaching commented:

> Science is the intellectual nursery for the next generation of scientists and technologists. Technology, like the mule, is strong and clever, but cannot breed its own next generation. This is because the next generation of first-class technologists needs an endowment of fresh outlook and knowledge, and new wisdom, if they are to work as creative people. It is the scientists who must give the next generation of technologists essential training or they will lack the deeper understanding which is part of their preparation.[3]

Rogers prefers the teaching of science in secondary schools to be concentrated upon the development of scientific understanding. J. Robert Oppenheimer stated his point of view as follows:

> Science and technology are symbiotic. . . . They are symbiotic not only because technology would be impoverished, blinded, and crippled were it not for the new knowledge which is sought and found for other reasons. Technology gives back again to science a rich reward in new instruments, new techniques and new powers. It is this incessant feedback and reciprocal fertilization which makes a sharp distinction between pure science and technology academic and dreary.[4]

The authors of the new science curricula prefer to develop courses around the inquiry processes and the conceptual structure of a discipline because these attributes of science are more stable. Technological and industrial applications of scientific principles are topics the teacher might bring to the course when it is advantageous to do so. These applications should be timely and local to be of educational value. While a part of the teacher's repertoire of supple-

[3] Rogers, E. M., "The Aims of Science Teaching: Teaching Science for Understanding." Appendix I. *Nuffield Physics, Teachers' Guide I.* London: Longmans/Penguin Books, 1966.

[4] Wolfle, Dale (ed.), *Symposium on Basic Research.* ("The Need for New Knowledge," J. Robert Oppenheimer). Washington, D.C.: Copyright 1959 by the American Association for the Advancement of Science, 1959, p. 9, 10.

mentary reading for the student, they are unsuitable as a structured component of a textbook or course of study.

SELECTED BIBLIOGRAPHY ON THE NATURE OF SCIENCE

To best understand the issues, problems, and trends in the teaching of secondary school science requires a familiarity with the scientific enterprise, its meaning and methods. Over 100 books and numerous articles have been published on the subject in the past decade. The following short bibliography will introduce the reader to the literature that describes science and some of the overlapping fields.

Barber, Bernard and Hirsch, Walter (eds.). *The Sociology of Science.* New York: The Free Press of Glencoe, 1962.

Beckner, L. V. *The Scientific Age: The Impact of Science on Society.* New Haven: Yale University Press, 1964.

Beckner, Morton. *The Biological Way of Thought.* New York: Columbia University Press, 1959.

Beveredge, W. I. B. *The Art of Scientific Investigation.* New York: W. W. Norton & Co., Inc., 1957.

Braithwaite, Richard B. *Scientific Explanation.* New York: Harper, 1960.

Butterfield, Herbert. *The Origins of Modern Science.* New York: The Free Press, 1957.

Caws, Peter. *The Philosophy of Science.* Princeton: Van Nostrand, 1965.

Conant, James B. *On Understanding Science.* New York: The New American Library, 1951.

Danto, Arthur, and Morgenbesser, Sidney (eds.). *Philosophy of Science.* Cleveland: The World Publishing Company, 1961.

Frank, Philipp. *Modern Science and Its Philosophy.* New York: Collier Books, 1961.

Hanson, N. R. *Patterns of Discovery.* Cambridge: Cambridge University Press, 1958.

Hempel, Carl C. *Aspects of Scientific Explanation.* New York: The Free Press, 1965.

Hempel, Carl C. *Philosophy of Natural Science.* Englewood Cliffs, N.J.: Prentice-Hall, Inc., 1966.

Holton, Gerald (ed.). *Science and Culture*. Boston: Houghton-Mifflin, 1965.

Kaplan, Norman (ed.). *Science and Society*. Chicago: Rand McNally & Co., 1965.

Klopfer, Leo. *History of Science Cases*. Chicago: Science Research Associates, 1965.

Kuhn, Thomas S. *The Structure of Scientific Revolutions*. Chicago: The University of Chicago Press, 1962.

Madden, Edward H. *The Structure of Scientific Thought*. Boston: Houghton-Mifflin, 1960.

Margenau, Henry. *Ethics and Science*. Princeton: Van Nostrand, 1964.

Meier, Richard L. *Science and Economic Development*. Cambridge: Technology Press of Massachusetts Institute of Technology, 1956.

Mehlberg, H. *The Reach of Science*. Toronto: University of Toronto Press, 1958.

Nagel, Ernest. *The Structure of Science*. New York: Harcourt, Brace & World Inc., 1961.

Nash, Leonard K. *The Nature of the Natural Sciences*. Boston: Little, Brown & Company, 1963.

Obler, Paul C., and Estrin, Herman A. *The New Scientist*. New York: Doubleday Co. Inc., 1962.

Pap, Arthur. *An Introduction to the Philosophy of Science*. Glencoe, Ill.: The Free Press of Glencoe, 1962.

Popper, Karl R. *The Logic of Scientific Discovery*. New York: Basic Books Inc., 1959.

Prior, Moody E. *Science and the Humanities*. Evanston: Northwestern University, 1962.

Rabinowitch, Eugene. *The Dawn of a New Age*. Chicago: University of Chicago Press, 1963.

Sarton, George. *Ancient Science and Modern Civilization*. Lincoln: University of Nebraska Press, 1954.

Storer, Norman W. *The Social System of Science*. New York: Holt, Rinehart and Winston, 1966.

Taton, René. *Reason and Chance in Scientific Discovery*. New York: Philosophical Library, 1957.

Toulmin, Stephen. *The Philosophy of Science*. New York: Harper, 1960.

Walker, Marshall. *The Nature of Scientific Thought*. Englewood Cliffs, N.J.: Prentice-Hall, 1963.

III

The Character of the Science Curriculum Reform

The stimulus for the curriculum reappraisal in science teaching came in one direction from university scientists and their concern about the poor preparation in science of entering college students. At the same time the shortage of technically trained manpower in America had reached a crisis. Together these conditions were enough to initiate a reform movement. While the problem was essentially one of university education, the immediate action was 'to get at the roots of the problem,' the high school science courses. In many respects the concern about pre-college science teaching is not recent. Within the past twenty-five years several efforts have been made to recast the science curriculum along new lines. The Progressive Education Association in its publication, *Science in General Education* (1938)[1] describes a program emphasizing the inquiry and social aspects of science. In 1945, a Harvard University Committee reporting in *General Education in a Free Society,*[2] recommended the teaching of high school science using broad integrative elements and scientific modes of inquiry set within cultural, historical and philosophical contexts. The stress was on the 'lasting values' of scientific information and experience. The President's Scientific Research Board (1947)[3] in a series of reports on the effectiveness of science instruction deplored the condition where students are taught science

[1] Progressive Education Association. *Science in General Education.* N.Y.: D. Appleton-Century Co., 1938.

[2] Report of the Harvard Committee. *General Education in a Free Society.* Cambridge: Harvard University Press, 1945.

[3] The President's Scientific Research Board (John R. Steelman, ed.). *Science and Public Policy,* Vol. 4. Wash. D.C.: Government Printing Office, 1947.

as "a world of natural laws, or orderly cause and effect, not a world of chance or arbitrary action." The Committee noted the lack of student interest in the physical sciences and suggested that "much more use could be made of the history of science, its adventure and dramatic action, which appeal strongly to young people's interests and arouse their imagination." Like the present reform movement, there was much interest shown in providing a suitable scientific background for students who might go to college. These are only a few of the special committee reports which, previous to 1950, suggested the need to reexamine the content and teaching methods of high school science, but the time was not propitious for action.

The conditions underlying the need for change were in part determined by changes in the social, cultural and economic structure of American life, but to a larger extent were determined by the number of recent advances in science. The typically conservative nature of curriculum development in schools reached a point where the old curriculum was seen as no longer effective for contemporary times. A revolt over the status quo of science courses had been fermenting for nearly two decades and it took only the launching of Sputnik I to ignite the spark. The result was a plethora of books criticizing American education from every angle and calling for a reform. The high school was the target chosen by the critics and it followed that this was where the curriculum reform was to begin, more specifically in the teaching of science and mathematics since these were areas crucial to our supply of technically trained manpower. As a country we had just been embarrassed by our lack of progress in the space program and we were determined that this should not happen again. However illogical the stimulus for the reform may have been, it brought about the most far-reaching school improvement programs America has ever experienced.

PRESSURES FOR A CURRICULUM REFORM

The public critics of science teaching felt that it had grown 'soft,' that it lacked 'rigor,' and was being taught from content that was out-of-date and had lost its significance within scientific fields. Instructional goals were criticized as too much pupil or 'life adjustment' centered. Science teachers were accused of not challenging the better students[4] and of making the whole program of instruction

[4] See Cole, Charles C., Jr. *Encouraging Scientific Talent*. New York: College Entrance Examination Board, 1956.

too easy with much time wasted on frills. Decreasing enrollments in physics and chemistry were attributed to "not presenting these subjects as they are known to the scientist." Furthermore, it was speculated that pupils would learn more if they were 'better' taught, that is, if improved methods of learning were used. The National Academy of Sciences—National Research Council[5] report on this issue in 1958, pointed out that human learning can be improved and that we already know more about how to do this than is being used to advantage.

Scientists writing about the high school science curriculum had such comments as "while biology, chemistry, and physics is taught, there is very little of the *science* of these subjects presented." Others felt that applied science and technology in high school textbooks were overly emphasized. They were not so much concerned about technology as topics of study as they were opposed to the teaching of technology as science thereby creating in the student's mind a false impression of the scientific enterprise. Like most of the critics they saw an inadequate science program for the kind of world young people now live in, but were more worried about how to prepare them for the social and scientific changes that will be even greater in the future. The character of western civilization was formed by science and technology, but where is this reflected in the secondary school curriculum? Why is it the very best of our young people have little real understanding of the scientific enterprise even after several years of science study and with good grades?[6] The major question is whether the existing science curricula are meeting the demands of the times and preparing young people for understanding the world in which they will be spending most of their life. And the answer, is *no*. Faculties spend more time expanding course offerings or revising content to meet immediate problems than creating a curriculum suitable to change and progress.

Teachers were widely criticized for a lack of education in the sciences they were teaching. In turn the blame was placed upon schools of education for emphasizing how to teach instead of what to teach. While it was well-known that these arguments were to a

[5] NAS-NRC Report of Conference. *Psychological Research in Education*, (Publication 643). Washington, D.C.: NAS-NRC, 1958.

[6] Mead, Margaret and Métraux, Rhoda. "Image of the Scientist Among High School Students: A Pilot Study," *Science*, CXXVI (Aug. 30, 1957), p. 348.

Science, the News, and the Public. A Report of the National Association of Science Writers, Inc. New York: New York Univ. Press, 1958.

large extent false and the statements exaggerated, they served the purpose of stimulating an 'educational revolution.' It was seldom mentioned directly that the shortage of technical manpower in the United States included the supply of qualified science teachers. This situation was predicted in 1953 at a Harvard University conference called by James B. Conant, then president of Harvard.[7] While the so-called 'teachers college' was blamed for the inadequacies of science teacher preparation, with their emphasis upon 'methods,' in reality they educate only a small per cent of the profession. As for their emphasis upon methods courses several surveys of science teacher preparation show that less than one-half of the teachers have had a methods course in the subject they are teaching. The misassignment of teachers outside of their subject is, however, widespread. It appears that a sizeable fraction of the science teachers of America are science teachers by administrative decision and not by training. But these and other teaching conditions in our high schools were not publicized during the crisis years;[8] to have done so would have slowed down the reform movement.

There was much criticism that the schools in general were out-of-date and failing to take advantage of modern technology in teaching. The advantages of television, programed textbooks, films, teaching machines, and new kinds of projectors were widely acclaimed. Among the first efforts in the curriculum reform were televised and filmed courses in biology, physics and chemistry. Later programed textbooks and teaching machines were developed, ostensibly to improve the pupil's learning efficiency. Architects sought to change the design of schools to make them more flexible, with features such

[7] Watson, F., Brandwein, P., Rosen, S. (eds.), *Critical Years Ahead in Science Teaching*. Cambridge, Mass.: Harvard University Press, 1953.

[8] Supporting data and more detailed discussion of science teacher preparation appears in the following publications:

National Science Foundation. *Secondary School Science and Mathematics Teachers, Characteristics and Service Loads* (NSF 63–10). Washington, D.C.: Government Printing Office, 1963.

Brown, Kenneth E. and Obourn, Ellsworth S. *Qualifications and Teaching Loads of Mathematics and Science Teachers*. (USOE Circular No. 575). Washington, D.C.: Government Printing Office, 1959.

Obourn, Ellsworth S. and Brown, Kenneth E. *Science and Mathematics Teachers in Public High Schools*. (OE–29045). Washington, D.C.: Government Printing Office, 1963.

NASDTEC-AAAS. *Guidelines for Preparation Programs of Teachers of Secondary School Science and Mathematics*. Washington, D.C.: American Association for the Advancement of Science, 1961.

as, moveable walls, larger rooms for team teaching, and smaller spaces or carrels for the individual student. The advantages of these innovations for the improvement of learning in science were assumed. It was soon to become obvious that automated machinery and changes in architecture and equipment do not constitute a curriculum reform and most of all they do not precede the movement. For example, longer class periods, larger or smaller class sizes or some combination are no better than the conventional curriculum if it is judged to be inadequate. Curriculum improvement is more a matter of human resources and insights than it is physical resources and inventions.

What were educators and school administrators doing at this time of educational crisis? Mostly they were plagued with problems of over-enrollment, teacher shortage, crowded buildings and financial limitation. What were the professional educational organizations doing? They were attempting to parry criticisms as they were made; they did not come forth with a philosophical basis for modern education nor did they define new goals to suit changing conditions within our society. What about educational research? The questions to be answered were practical ones: How do children learn science? What are good methods of teaching to obtain specific instructional goals? How should a curriculum be organized to improve learning? What instructional tools are most effective for certain kinds of learning? How should teachers be educated? Useful answers were not available. The result was that educational research has had almost no influence on the science curriculum reform.

The ferment and turmoil about science teaching during the 1950's led organized groups of scientists to attempt to improve the situation. They read the existing high school textbooks in their subject fields and examined local curriculum guides. They were not happy with what they found either in content or organization. It was obvious that attempts had been made to keep courses up-to-date but this was done by adding new bits and pieces of knowledge to the old content. Practically no change in the conceptual structure of the subject matter was apparent. Actually few changes along this line had been made in this century, although there were efforts to do so.[9] Textbooks over

[9] See Hurd, Paul DeHart. *Biological Education in American Secondary Schools 1890–1960*. Washington, D.C.: American Institute of Biological Sciences, 1961. The patterns of curriculum reforms described here for biology are similar to those for chemistry and physics.

the years had grown by accretion; seldom does one find a traditional topic dropped from a text or course. Knowledge within a scientific discipline is cumulative and self-corrective, but in school courses it is represented as fragments to be added to the curriculum rather than to revise the structure of the science.

The preliminary examination of the science curriculum problems led to one positive and unanimous decision among the reformers: that no amount of effort could bring existing science courses into an organization acceptable to the scientific community. This meant little could be done to bring existing courses into line with modern science, and it would be necessary to start from the beginning and develop new courses. The movement became, therefore, not one of curriculum revision but of reform.

THE SCIENCE CURRICULUM REFORMER SEEKS NEW GOALS

By 1957 different groups of scientists and mathematicians became sufficiently concerned about the teaching of these subjects to decide "something needs to be done about the situation." We have already noted they regarded their task as one of starting from the beginning with no commitments to either the content or goals of existing textbooks, courses of study, or curricula. And to this may be added any defineable theory or philosophy of education. Briefly, the usual way to build a course of study is to establish the objectives, state these as operationally as possible, and then select the subject matter in these terms. Sometimes there is a consideration of the pupil and the social conditions under which he lives. This may be the way an educator builds a curriculum but it is not the way a scientist would do it, or did. Essentially the scientist poses the question: What does it take to provide a valid picture of my discipline that might be learned by a high school student? His next step is to begin writing the course as he sees it; his guide is intuition. But what about the goals; they come *last* after the course is completed, when the question is raised: What have we accomplished? The goals emerge in retrospect from an examination of the completed product and are identified in terms of conceptual schemes and inquiry processes. The focus on these objectives for science teaching is a distinctive characteristic of the present reform.

Systematic and productive knowledge is seen as a primary goal of education in the new curricula. To be sure, most courses of study in the past have had the attainment of knowledge as a major outcome. Typically a course of study is represented by a classified listing of the information to be acquired, organized around larger topics called units or chapters. The subject matter of the units is chosen on the basis of criteria such as, "meeting the needs of pupils" and "sampling the discipline." There is a different point of view represented in the new science curricula. Here one finds that the content of science, with its concepts, theories, laws and modes of inquiry, is given, not chosen. To understand a science as a discipline requires knowing the 'right' concepts and methods. In other words, the criteria for the selection of course content arises from the discipline, or one might say that it is the discipline that chooses the curriculum. A course of study is also seen as a plan for knowing, a way of getting to know. The learning activities are those of experimenting, observing, computing, inferring, inventing, evaluating, and many other *ways* of knowing. In traditional science curricula, knowing means acquiring a fund of useful information. Knowledge of this sort is seen as having only limited or current value and is unsuited for coping with change and new advances. Knowledge in the context of a discipline provides for its own continuous growth, and serves to increase the intellectual capacity of the learner. It also has certain logical consequences within the structure of the discipline, providing perspective and relationships, and projects into unstudied problems where it can be used to predict or form generalizations. The emphasis in the new curricula is not on what the student will need to know for the test next week but to what extent his learning of this week will influence his future performance within the course and in the years to come.

In the new science curriculum competence in learning is not limited to being able to answer questions from an assignment or to work the problems of the laboratory. A student is expected to know more than an answer; this might include the restricted meaning of the topic, its modification for different contexts, or its expression in quantitative terms. To know something is to have insight into its meaning in terms of the laws, theories or conceptual schemes of science. It is in this way what is learned becomes useful for thinking and problem solving. Another way of stating the results of learning is whether the student understands the structure of a science: Does he see the relevance of the concepts, principles, and inquiries constituting the discipline? Has he developed an intuitive capacity allowing him to go beyond the subject matter described as the course (a test might be his ability to reason by analogy)? And, are his powers of reasoning those that characterize the science he is studying?

An examination of the new experimental science courses will show they are more theory and concept oriented than conventional courses. Some critics have interpreted this to mean they are less practical, particularly so since they lack technological information. But there is a more fundamental reason for this orientation, since in science practical knowledge is derived from basic concepts, laws, principles and theories. 'Getting practical' essentially means let's start thinking about the situation in terms of what we know. To teach practical knowledge without a basis in concepts and theories is to convey sterile, inert information which at best usually fits only a single instance. With the amount of knowledge there is available today we can rarely afford information limited to one example or a single problem.

During the curriculum reform there has been considerable emphasis upon the importance of developing breadth of knowledge as well as depth. What this means has been the subject of much discussion and gross misinterpretation. In each of the new course projects, the number of concepts to be formed during the school year has been drastically reduced when compared with traditional courses in the same subject. This makes it possible to teach each topic in depth, and give the student greater command over the concept. Breadth as it is used in the curriculum studies does not mean exposure to a wide range of information, but rather the study of fewer topics learned to the point where they have wide application and generalizability. Breadth of understanding is thus the product of studying a topic in depth.

What about pupil motivation in the new curriculum? The assumption is made that a pupil will develop a positive attitude toward learning if he is allowed to pursue knowledge on his own; to observe, explore, organize and interpret with a minimum of direction. In doing so he is likely to acquire some of the same feeling of satisfaction that motivates the scholar in his endeavors. The new curriculum projects attempt to make the reward for learning intrinsic, arising from the successful search for understanding.

To be a successful learner in the new courses the student needs to be proficient in modes of scientific inquiry. He needs to learn how different kinds of knowledge are advanced, communicated, recorded, and interpreted. He must not only understand investigatory procedures, but his own part in the process as well; and a very active part it is. One purpose of science teaching is to develop rational rather than impulsive individuals. This requires knowledge in a form productive of thought, and the intellectual processes that make it function and the willingness to use both. These are attributes not only important to the development of scientific literacy in young people, but essential to a general education in science. The entire cogency of the curriculum reformer's position consists of having young people understand the conceptual and methodological components of the various disciplines of science. Only in this way is it possible to appreciate the intellectual history of science in Western Civilization and its place in contemporary society.

One aspect of science receiving considerable emphasis in the reform movement is its 'open-endedness,' 'cumulative' or revisionary characteristic. Much of science teaching in the past was presented as dogma, and students did not have the opportunity to learn that what they study currently is only a phase in the growth of scientific knowledge. New developments are not seen as extensions of the past, nor is the incertitude of current knowledge explained. An appreciation of uncertainty and change is seen as an important goal of instruction in the new curriculum.[10] The educational implications of this goal are far reaching. In the past, science teaching has attempted to focus on established principles and a considerable number of studies were conducted to find which principles should be taught. These were presented in terms of "meeting the immediate needs of pupils." But this is a world of change and progress in which not only aspects of science, but social, cultural, and economic conditions become obsolete. It is as Robert M. Hutchins has pointed out a world that is "getting newer all the time." Yesterday's and today's intellectual maps and theories are not likely to be adequate for tomorrow's decisions. One way of meeting this problem is to teach young people to expect change and then use curricula and methods of instruction to help them to do so.

[10] Some background for this point of view is found in Kuhn, Thomas S., *The Structure of Scientific Revolutions*. Chicago: The University of Chicago Press, 1962.

The current educational emphasis upon creativity, inquiry, intuitive interpretations, learning to learn, independent study, discovery, and autonomous learning are each reflections of this point of view.

The goals for science teaching as they have emerged during the curriculum reform are not subject to neat statements that can be listed as an introduction to a course of study in the usual way. What is expressed is more a point of view or rationale for the teaching of science. This point of view lacks the societal orientation usually found in statements of educational goals. The 'new' goals of science teaching are drawn entirely from the disciplines of science. Social problems, individual needs, life problems and other means used in the past to define educational goals are not considered. The goals of instruction are not differentiated for local schools or for individuals. If the discipline of science is to be the source of educational goals, then differences are not possible without violating the structure of science. To do otherwise would be teaching un-science, a major criticism of the traditional curriculum. Thus we find the reformers define educational goals within the framework of science as they are reflected in the separate science disciplines. Their logic is simple and straightforward: this is what we know with some degree of reliability; this is how we find out about what we know; and this is how it all fits into the big picture—conceptual schemes. Now then, whatever personal or social problems involving science are to be solved must begin with authentic concepts and with fruitful processes of inquiry.

THE SELECTION OF CONTENT FOR SCIENCE COURSES

Certainly the most important problem in the development of a new curriculum is the selection of content that is to make up the courses of study. The present reform began with a criticism of the content of conventional science courses as something trivial and nonscientific in character. Whatever is taught always represents the point of view of some individual or group. Either implicitly or explicitly there are reasons justifying the instructional materials. Sometimes the reason for teaching a topic is not very clear; it is simply that it is always taught, like the cross-section of a root in biology, classes of levers in physics, and processes for making steel in chemistry. Before 1920 the majority of science textbooks were written by scientists teaching in college. They chose the content that seemed reasonable to them and in most cases the research or special interests of the author was quite conspicuous. For the next third of a century university scientists lost interest in pre-college science teaching; they had problems with their own courses generated by the exponential growth of scientific knowledge. The high school science teacher was left to his own devices to determine "what knowledge would be of most worth" to present young people in about 175 clock hours of time available for a high school course. The simplest way to solve the problem is to select a textbook either on one's own or from the state's recommended list. Unfortunately lists of criteria for textbook selection usually have more to say about the book's physical appearance, durability and make-up than its learning components. It is rare to see a list of criteria that specifies a conceptual organization, the inquiry processes to be emphasized, or identifies the teaching mode that offers the best chance for realizing the stated educational goals.

Serious efforts have been made in the past twenty-five years to research what should be taught in science courses. Typically these studies resulted in a list of science topics or principles in rank order of importance for teaching. The most important difference between these studies is the criterion used to form the original list of principles or topics to be taught. Some of the criteria used were: 1) an analysis of allusions to science found in newspapers and popular magazines (the assumption was made that young people should be prepared to understand the science found in materials they are likely to read frequently); 2) an analysis of items found in the final tests of many teachers (here the assumption was that teachers ask questions on final tests about topics they judge to be the most important); 3) an analysis of common superstitions and misconceptions about science (the rationale was that courses should concentrate on topics about which young people have developed erroneous beliefs); 4) a tabulation of the everyday activities of adult men and women to determine the science information they found useful; 5) the study of students and their interests and needs, and the building of courses to satisfy these needs; 6) the use of parents to describe what it is they wish they had studied in high school science courses (these topics form the curriculum for their children); 7) the identification of "persistent life problems," such as, health, conservation, family life (and from the components of these problems establish courses to help young people meet these problems); 8) an analysis and synthesis of topics found in widely used textbooks (frequency of an item was a measure of its importance for teaching); 9) an examination of local courses of study for commonalities (here the rationale was that the opinions of classroom teachers who develop course guides are more worthy than those of curriculum makers who do not work directly with students); 10) the tabulation and ranking of questions from standardized tests, regents examinations, and college entrance tests (this was seen as a means to provide a curriculum base without local bias); 11) enlisting 'expert' opinion on what should be taught by submitting a list of 50–100 'principles' to scientists, science educators, or curriculum developers to rate the importance of each for inclusion in a science course; 12) appointing a committee, typically from membership in a professional society, with the directive "to develop a better course of study"; 13) recognizing that there were nearly always a few topics that had to be taught as 'legal requirements,' such as, health and safety topics, the 'evils of alcohol and tobacco,' and others; 14) and that there were some topics that were *not* to be taught in certain states, for example, organic evolution and human sexual reproduction; 15) tabulating and ranking the science vocabulary found in textbooks and courses of study to isolate topics of high 'importance.' The results from these studies were used to *revise* the existing curriculum, usually by giving more attention to some topics if they ranked high on the criterion measure, and less attention if they ranked low. Most of the time the curriculum revision was carried on without regard to the structure of science or underlying philosophical, social, and learning assumptions. One is reminded of Aristotle's observation after visiting the schools of Athens in 300 B.C.

> There are doubts concerning the business of education since all people do not agree on those things which they would have a child taught, both with respect to improvement in virtue and a happy life; nor is it clear whether the object of it should be to improve the reason or rectify the morals. From the present mode of education we cannot determine with certainty to which men incline, whether to instruct a child in which will be useful to him in life, or what tends to virtue, or what is excellent; for all these things have their separate defenders.

None of the curriculum reformers made use of these research studies in the development of the new science curricula. Several reasons are apparent: 1) for the most part the studies were done without reference to a clearly defined educational theory; 2) the results of the studies were not validated within the conceptual structure of science for significance and relevance. Certainly the studies were attempting to determine what out of the wealth of scientific information should be taught, but the procedures used resulted in a consensus of topics that were either interesting, popular, or useful regardless of their place, if any, in the scheme of science. A long time ago, John Dewey recognized the danger of this approach to curriculum development and commented as follows:

> One method is the scrappy one of picking up isolated materials just because they happen to be familiar objects within the pupil's experience, and of merely extending and deepening the range of pupil's familiarity, and then passing on to something else. No amount of this will make an introduction to education, to say nothing of science, for an introduction leads or draws into a subject, while this method never, save by accident, gets the pupil within range of problems and explanatory methods of science.[11]

Similar studies, although fewer in number, were made to analyze the characteristics of 'problem solving' in science and to identify aspects of the 'scientific method.' Lists of attitudes, skills and methodological descriptions were developed and frequently served as objectives for the teaching of science. While the results of these studies often served as the basis for an opening or final chapter in science textbooks, the processes of science were not truly integrated into courses. For the most part the results of these studies did not present a valid picture of the inquiry processes as they are used in science. For example, there was little regard for theory, models, operational definitions, and the conceptual structures that help to make observations intelligible. Interpretation of data was defined as the means by which observations are described such as, graphs, tables, or measurements. How observations become data was typically omitted from courses. The problem-solving procedures identified were more characteristic of applied research, engineering, and the reporting of experiments than of scientific discovery. The human component in scientific investigation was almost never mentioned. In other words, the science subjects of the traditional high school curriculum were for the most part quite at odds with their parent disciplines both in content and methodology.

[11] Dewey, John. "Method in Science Teaching," *General Science Quarterly*, (Nov. 1916). 1:(1), 3.

THE SELECTION OF COURSE CONTENT FOR THE NEW CURRICULA

The scientists responsible for the new science courses found little of value in the criteria that curriculum makers had been using for several decades to select subject matter. They rejected first all notions that it was possible in any way to sample or 'cover' a scientific discipline in a high school course. What is worth knowing is the crucial question. In the past there was much attention given to selecting useful or interesting topics, but this was regarded as too much like window shopping—lacking significant organization. Concentrating on the 'science' that is at the moment attracting attention in the public press could miss the mainstream of science, since what is reported most frequently are technical achievements, such as, space probes, linear accelerators, transistors, jet engines, heart transplants, hybrid corn, or synthetic fibers. This situation is analogous to attempting to teach history from current events or mathematics by programing computers. The scientists in each of the new projects sought to answer the question of what constitutes *an education in a science* and were not deeply concerned at the onset with the specifics of subject matter content.

If one thinks of a high school science course as an organized body of subject matter in either biology, physics, chemistry or earth science there is only one authentic source of topics to draw upon and this is the parent discipline. The very nature of a discipline is that it is an organization of knowledge and its significant concepts, principles, conceptual schemes, laws and theories can be identified. The curriculum task is first one of identifying the major over-arching ideas that currently characterize the mainstream of thinking within the discipline. The committees for each of the science curriculum projects have been able to do this, with varying degrees of clarity. Some curriculum developers are critical of this approach because it appears to disregard the cultural context of the curriculum. Two answers are apparent: 1) the knowledge that comprises a discipline is the organized knowledge of the culture, there is nowhere else to look; 2) the compelling forces of contemporary society are those of science, and it is through an understanding of the scientific enterprise that the conditions and problems of contemporary civilization are best interpreted and dealt with.

The concepts and principles that are to constitute a science course should be those that present a modern picture of the discipline; these may be described as the "key concepts" or "representative ideas." The selection is not random but must represent the logical structure of a discipline. These components which serve to unify courses are called strands. Priority is given to conceptual schemes at the advancing front of science since they are most likely to influence the future of science and be contemporary with the life span of the learner. This is to say, if young people are to understand problems and conditions brought about by new thinking in a science, they are more likely to do so with subject matter that prepares for the acquisition of new knowledge. Since there will always be more knowledge in a discipline worthy of teaching than can be taught in a school year, what is chosen should offer the best promise for allowing the student to learn on his own after he leaves the course. It is as John Dewey states in *Experience and Education,* ". . . the central problem of education is to select the kind of present experiences that live fruitfully and creatively in subsequent experiences."

With an emphasis upon the larger conceptual structure of science the student is in a better position to recognize and understand changes in scientific knowledge. The specificity of the content of traditional courses was such as to create the illusion knowledge in science is true, fixed, and certain. When a course is built around conceptual schemes new developments are more likely to fit into what the student already knows and what is more important he is likely to appreciate the relevance of these changes.

In the present science curriculum reform a major effort is made to have the active, the knowing, the inquiry phase of science strongly represented. In previous course developments most of the concern has been with updating the informational content and assuring adequate coverage is attained. *Understanding* science, however, is more a matter of appreciating its modes of inquiry than it is inventorying the current status of its achievements. Science is, as someone has described, "more a verb than a noun." The processes of inquiry help us to learn how the knowledge of science is obtained, its parameters and probabilities, and what it means today. If these attributes of scientific knowledge are not a significant part of instruction the teaching of science becomes a dogma or, as Joseph J. Schwab has described it, "a rhetoric of conclusions." For each of the sciences there are methods of inquiry and investigation by which the field is organized, discoveries made, problems attacked, and the accumulated knowledge brought into order through models and theories. In considering subject matter for science courses it is essential to choose topics that exemplify scientific methods of inquiry and allow the exercise of them. Some of these topics should be selected because they illustrate certain doubts and ignorance in science. Understanding science means the student has a knowledge of its significant concepts, a command of its inquiry processes, and appreciates the interaction of both.

The inquiry skills best suited for science teaching are those which are generalizable and widely applicable for both learning and problem solving. These are the intellectual skills that make it possible for a student to organize his thinking, to recognize and use relevant data in a meaningful way, and to perform generally as a rational person. These skills go beyond the assembling and recording of observations and the interpretation of data. They include the use of the interpretive themes of science—laws, principles, theories, hypotheses, models—which make data meaningful in a wider context than specific problems. The new science courses incorporate modern concepts of inquiry in their laboratory program, but it is less apparent in the textbooks. The Biological Sciences Curriculum Study prepared special materials to use in conveying an understanding of the processes of science as they are used in the biological sciences. These are called "Invitations to Enquiry" and appear in the BSCS teacher's handbook.

There are factors working to influence the subject matter of courses that are frequently beyond the control of the curriculum maker, although they have a profound effect upon the curriculum as it reaches the learner. The most important of these is teaching competence, for it is the teacher who makes course content available to the student, and his background in the subject and his style of teaching must reflect an understanding and commitment to scientific inquiry and concept formation or the curriculum with these goals is nullified. Inquiry oriented laboratory problems can be written but if the experiments are not carried out the goal is not likely to be reached.

A subject matter criterion of the present reform is, other things being equal, that placement of a topic in the science curriculum should be at the lowest grade level at which the material can be understood by most pupils. The result has been to assign a number of topics to earlier grades. In the Physical Science Study Committee physics project it was assumed the material on sound could just as well be learned in the junior high school years. The BSCS writers had the same feeling about natural history. In neither case was there a recommendation such materials be eliminated from the education of the pupil.

The current curriculum reform looks to the special disciplines as the sources of information to be taught. This is more than saying that the discipline is our only source of authentic knowledge; it includes the organization or structure of this material which goes beyond the content selected, but is dependent upon it. Since it is always possible to choose from any discipline a range of concepts that represents its organization, it is possible to devise several different kinds of courses based upon the same science and to have each represent the structure of the field. The four textbook versions of the BSCS, all for beginning students yet each different in its biological emphasis, are an example of how this may be accomplished. The four textbook versions of the Chemical Education Material Study, the PSSC and Harvard Project physics courses, and the two earth science programs are other examples. In each instance the choice of course content is representative of the discipline, and the methods of inquiry developed are those which are required to sense the nature of the field.

ORGANIZATION AND SEQUENCE IN THE NEW SCIENCE CURRICULUM

After decisions are made about the content of a course, the materials need to be organized into a sequence of topics that will promise achievement of the objectives of the course. There are two dimensions to the organization of a science curriculum. One is the vertical structure between grade levels that gives coherence to the entire program from kindergarten through grade twelve. This is accomplished through the use of conceptual schemes and basic inquiry processes. The horizontal organization, within a school subject, is a more refined approach based upon the concepts and inquiry processes peculiar to a specific science. Our concern here is with the horizontal structure of a science course.

Traditionally, science textbooks have been organized into a series of problems, units, or simply chapters. Each unit is largely self-sufficient and all are written at about the same level of conceptualization. There is little reference to what precedes or follows a topic. This gives rise to the feeling students have that once they have studied a chapter, they 'have had it' as though the whole thing can now be dismissed. At times two or three chapters may be dependent upon each other, but this results from a long topic rather than a concept dependency.

In the new science courses the assumption is made that disciplined knowledge suggests its own organization. One characteristic of a discipline is that there is a pattern to its concepts. The major concepts provide the focus for the organization of the contributing facts and concepts. If the subject matter of the course follows the logical organization of the discipline, it is assumed that the learner will be in a better position to understand new materials because they are most likely to be logical extensions of previous learning. In this sense the curriculum is 'open-ended,' or continuous. In a problem-centered curriculum it is only possible to learn more about the problem, whereas in a discipline-centered curriculum the concepts grow in meaning and comprehensiveness with new experiences. In a problem or unit approach the attention is upon collecting information to solve the problem, whereas in the discipline approach the focus is upon organization and relationships of knowledge. There is little argument that a discipline-centered organization is a specialist's field. This has given use to the expression "learning like a scientist." The curriculum maker's task is one of preparing learning materials that make it possible for young people to follow the intellectual map of the biologist, physicist or chemist. It is not assumed this will be accomplished all at once but will be developed gradually within a course.

Another characteristic of a discipline-centered course is that successive ideas can be presented at increasingly higher levels of meaning. One concept is based on another and both contribute to understanding a third. The topics toward the end of a textbook are late in the course because they need a reservoir of supporting concepts to make them intelligible. In contrast to traditional course organizations the new textbooks are tightly sequenced and to omit a chapter or change its order is to damage the learning of all that follows.

Inquiry skills in a course are organized in a hierarchical pattern from simple to more complex processes. As a student progresses within a course he is expected to become more critical in his observations, to represent experimental data more accurately, and to improve his interpretation of data by using models and theories. As investigatory skills are developed in the laboratory the student is expected to need fewer and fewer directions about how to proceed on a problem. The *Chemical Bond Approach* (CBA) laboratory manual provides an excellent example of this type of organization. After the student has worked his way through a number of experiments he is presented with just the statement of a problem for which he devises an experimental procedure. For example, in experiment 45 of the manual the only directions to the student are: "Conduct an extensive laboratory investigation to obtain data that can be used to advance an argument about the structure of solutions."[12] In a series of laboratory investigations the student is expected to develop a concept of what is meant by experimental errors, such as *absolute, relative, constant,* and *random.* He learns the significance of each and how each may be recognized.

There is a successful but incomplete effort in the new science courses to sequence the subject matter concepts and the inquiry skills so both are available at the time a class or laboratory problem is to be studied. This is only reasonable since a systematic approach to any problem situation requires a potentially relevant fund of information, concepts, and principles and the modes of inquiry required to focus the array of data. If the appropriate knowledge or the intellectual processes are not available the problem remains or improper conclusions are drawn. Some of the difficulties young people have in learning science result from not having acquired, at the time they are needed, the inquiry skills and concepts demanded by the task. Both kinds of competencies are built in a gradual fashion; the simpler phases are developed first and tested with simple problems followed with increasingly more complex problems. If prior experiences in a course have been improperly sequenced or the student is remiss in learning he will soon be hopelessly lost and will need to resort to rote memorization to get through the course.

A well organized curriculum is a succession of backgrounds that make the next steps in learning reasonable. There is a planned redundancy in the materials, not in the sense of repetition, but rather in maintaining the cumulative character of the learning, building upon earlier experiences rather than simply adding to them. In this way problems are never approached cold since the prerequisites are

[12] Chemical Bond Approach Project, *Investigating Chemical Systems.* St. Louis: Webster Division, McGraw-Hill Book Co., Inc., 1963, p. 69.

planned in advance and what is learned currently provides a foundation for what is to come. Gilbert Finley describes this organization for PSSC physics as follows: "The intellectual thrust of the basic ideas is brought out sequentially through using those which are introduced early to illuminate other ideas in a chain that comprises an introductory view of the structure of physics."[13]

Because the modern science curriculum is tightly sequenced and discipline-centered some critics have felt the range of abilities and educational backgrounds of students are not considered. Sometimes this may be true, however, more often the problem is one of not acquainting the student with the nature of the new approach and the learning expectations which are not like those of the traditional courses. The student comes to high school with almost a decade of education behind him and at the present time he is quite likely not to have had modern elementary school science as a background.[14] The new goals of science teaching are more different than difficult. For each of the new science courses, earth science, biology, chemistry, and physics, there is a wider choice of textbooks and supplementary teaching materials reflecting similar goals than has been available to schools in the past. "Advanced topics," "research problems," multiple texts, "special materials," and "open-ended" experiments provide for a wide range of differences among students. The American Institutes for Research in their project PLAN are developing as many as seven alternative approaches to a single science unit.[15]

CRITICISMS OF THE CONVENTIONAL SCIENCE COURSES

The concerns that led the Federal government to finance the development of new science courses for the high school suggest at least a dissatisfaction with the older programs. Since each of the new curriculum projects developed their courses differently from those of the past we may again assume a disagreement with the older practices. However, it is difficult to find in the curriculum literature an explicit statement of the weaknesses of the traditional science cur-

[13] Finley, Gilbert C., "Secondary School Physics: The Physical Science Study Committee," *American Journal of Physics,* 28:292, March, 1960.

[14] Hurd, Paul DeH., and Gallagher, James J., *New Directions in Elementary Science Teaching*. Belmont: Wadsworth Publishing Co., Inc., 1968.

[15] Flanagan, John C., "Functional Education for the Seventies." *Phi Delta Kappan,* 49:1:27 (Sept. 1967).

riculum. We must infer these inadequacies from a comparison of older textbooks with their counterparts in the new curriculum.[16]

In the traditional courses the assumption is frequently made that the easiest way to learn science is through technological applications. The scientists developing the new programs do not believe the true nature of science can be taught in this way. In support of their position they point to the number of students having had high school science who are unable to distinguish science from technology.

Science courses in the past have been overwhelmingly fact oriented. While facts have use, a familiarity with them is not the ingredient that represents what we know about science. Curriculum developers in the past have been more careful to have their materials factually accurate than to have them true to concept. While facts may be true they can be trivial in that they lack explanatory power. At other times, a concept may change in meaning so that the facts it harbors, while still accurate as observations, no longer hold the meaning they once had. To know that carbon dioxide and water are used in photosynthesis explains little about the modern concept; 100 years ago this information was a step forward. To speak of conventional science courses as outmoded has more to do with the current conceptual structure of a discipline than it does the specifics of course content.

Traditional courses are "bits and pieces of knowledge" without conceptual unity. Each unit consists of several topics which are defined and explained, and the next chapter consists of other topics treated in the same way with little build-up from one topic to the next. Tiers of explanation are seldom found and conceptual bridges from unit to unit are weak or lacking.

Laboratory work in conventional courses is poorly related to course objectives and consists of exercises for developing manipulatory skills rather than a problem in systematic thinking. Successful progress in the course seldom depends upon the student's understanding the results of a series of experiments integrally related to the science concepts within the course. Years of effort have also produced "experiments" which are essentially fool-proof, that is, the

[16] For a valid distinction between the old and new programs it is necessary to examine commonly used textbooks in the older curriculum that were published previous to *1957*. New editions of many of the non-subsidized textbooks have adopted some of the goals and a conceptual organization characteristic of the new programs.

right answer is certain to emerge for everyone in class if the laboratory directions are followed. For each of the special sciences there are other negative reactions; in most instances these have to do with the failure of laboratory work to reflect the modes of scientific inquiry as they are known to the scientist.

A major criticism of traditional science courses is the dogmatic way in which they are taught. Science is presented as a body of information verified and certain. The incertitudes, probabilities and revisionary characteristics of scientific knowledge are not presented. Courses present the knowledge without reference to its development, its current status, and what it is we do not know about the topic.[17]

Characteristic features of the scientific enterprise are its modes of inquiry and its human attributes; both are widely neglected in school science. Science is taught more as an anthology of achievements than as human intelligence at work seeking to refine man's understanding of the natural world. Emphasis is more upon describing what we know than how we know; upon answering questions than upon deciding what questions should be asked.

Much of what is taught is at a descriptive level, such as, the characteristics of the halogens, the organs of a frog, or the particles within an atom. There is a minimum of theory and explanatory concepts to make observations and data meaningful.

The investigative nature of science is typically limited to a section at the beginning or at the end of a course. It is something apart from the main content. Moreover, it is treated as a 'scientific method' as though such a method exists and if followed will lead to 'discoveries.' At other times there is a presentation of 'problem solving,' a series of five or six steps in order ending with a 'conclusion.' Such a procedure may be useful in engineering, product design, and certain developmental activities, but it is not characteristic of the scientific endeavor.

The style of instruction in much of high school science teaching is regarded as ineffective. One focus of complaint is the 'telling' of science, a routine in which the teacher does most of the talking, supplemented by a few demonstrations and films. Progress through

[17] An example of a different approach is found in American Geological Institute (Robert L. Heller, Editor), *Geology and Earth Sciences Sourcebook for Elementary and Secondary Schools*. New York: Holt, Rinehart and Winston, Inc. 1962. In this book many units include a discussion and a listing of unsolved problems on particular topics.

the course is rapid and few topics are developed to the point where they are really understood by the student. In part, this is the result of too many topics in the course and a compulsion on the part of the teacher to finish the text. This is a carry-over from the time when a course was meant to 'cover' a discipline, a position recognized as no longer tenable. One result of this teaching procedure is that students forget much of what they are taught and more forgetting than remembering is the outcome of instruction.

In summary, the major criticisms of the conventional curriculum are: (1) high school science courses do not reflect science as science is known by scientists, either in content or method; and (2) learning is inefficient and students are unable to make intellectual use of what they learn.

EMERGING CRITICISMS OF THE NEW SCIENCE COURSES

The developers of the new science programs set out to remedy the complaints about the old curriculum. Their efforts were more intuitive than specifically planned and the courses that emerged represent innumerable compromises. Financing for the new science programs came mostly from the National Science Foundation (NSF) and its policies indirectly influenced the final product. In effect the NSF directive was that "new" courses were to be improved in content and were to be for the same student population enrolled in the corresponding traditional courses. This limitation did not allow the invention of completely new courses or a major reorganization of the science curriculum. Thus some of the shortcomings of the new courses are more a responsibility of the funding agency than of the project directors. In another way, if one considers that the present reform is only the first phase in a continuing effort to develop the most effective science curriculum possible, then the major criticisms of today's materials represent suggestions for newer directions.

Since the new science programs were developed without reference to each other these high school courses are in many ways more specialized than the disciplines they represent. To be sure, some content from chemistry was added to BSCS biology and the early chapters of PSSC physics include astronomy and chemical concepts; however, the intra-subject connections are weak and the broader meanings of science obscured. Topics from other sciences are used primarily to expand the meaning of a specific topic rather than to illustrate the developing unity between the sciences. One result of this approach is illustrated in the BSCS courses where the way in which chemistry is used has caused some local school curriculum committees to recommend the teaching of chemistry before biology, but this was never the intent of the BSCS authors.

So far the best correlation between the new science courses is found in the emphasis upon the nature of scientific inquiry. While it was not planned as a curriculum theme, it does appear in each of the new course projects. One may speculate that in the long run the inquiry processes may be a more effective theme for integrating science courses than concepts from biology, physics, chemistry, and the earth sciences.

In terms of the rather narrow science context within which the new courses are written they are only slightly improved over traditional programs. The subject matter for the most part lacks humanistic, social, and historical perspectives. When these aspects of science are not dealt with the general education goal of a course is suspect. One limitation of a discipline-centered approach, with all of its advantages, is that it tends to encourage courses with a professional or specialist orientation rather than a liberal education point of view. An education in the sciences becomes a scientific education only in the context of the disciplines of science. Science teaching becomes general education only in a humanistic context. The relationship between the sciences and social sciences and humanities is no different in the new than in the old science curriculum.

The new curriculum is restricted largely to the scientific disciplines found in traditional programs. Some exceptions do occur in the new earth science courses. In terms of significance, for example, the sciences of anthropology, oceanography, human ecology, and biophysics among others are poorly represented. The present reform has been more active in improving the content of the classical school sciences than in broadening the base of education in the sciences.

A common criticism of the new science courses is that they are too difficult for the average student. The decreasing enrollment in physics is attributed to this cause and the BSCS found it necessary to develop a fourth version of its tenth grade course for the slow learner. While the criticism is common the reasons are not so apparent. As we have mentioned before new courses are sometimes difficult because they have different goals and the learning expectations are not familiar to the student. For example, he may for years have been a successful student because he found memorizing the appropriate terms for a test easy; his grades were "A." In the new program he has tests that require him to use concepts to interpret situations he has never studied. He is also expected to use what he learned in September to answer questions on a test given in April. No longer is it possible for a student to say "I've had that," as though it was all over and could be forgotten. This will require a change in attitude or he will continue to have difficulty with the subject. Any science curriculum can be made 'easy' or 'hard' by the way it is taught. The problem is somewhat more complicated when the goals and learning expectations are also new for the teacher. This is one reason why the developers of the experimental programs wanted teachers to attend briefing sessions or special institutes before teaching the new courses. It was recognized from the onset of these projects that they would require a style of teaching different from conventional courses or students would have learning difficulties. Guesses, made by classroom observers, suggest perhaps as many as fifty per cent of the teachers using the new curriculum materials are not teaching the course in a manner consistent with the specified goals. [18] In these instances it is reasonable students will find the course difficult to learn. A rigorous course in science does not mean it is difficult to learn although this has been an interpretation.

There is criticism the new courses are too long; "it's impossible to do everything that is expected in one school year." There are several factors contributing to this situation. One of these is the teacher's experience with the material; the BSCS staff found it took several years before a teacher felt reasonably well organized to manage the course properly. But more important, I have seen no pronouncements from any of the new curriculum projects to the effect the textbook as published was to be covered in a school year. The project directors have repeatedly emphasized the importance of teaching each concept in the sequence in sufficient depth to give it meaning before going on to the next topic or chapter. While progress in the course is expected, finishing the last chapter is not. Differences among pupils are a third factor having something to do with the difficulty level of a course.

[18] One weakness of most summer and academic year institutes preparing science teachers for the new courses is the failure to inform them about the different learning conditions and the new modes of instruction demanded by the innovative curriculum.

The range of differences is the same for the old curriculum as it is for the new. The question can only be whether modern science is harder to learn than traditional science or a conceptually oriented course more difficult to learn than a fact laden course. There seems to be no supporting data for either of these assumptions.

PROBLEMS OF INNOVATION AND CHANGE

Whenever the frame of reference is changed in a curriculum an immediate reaction is somehow the 'new' is in error because the 'old' has been with us so long. Almost immediately comparisons are made between the old and new courses and there is much concern about which program is better. Educational researchers will pair classes on the basis of the old and new approaches, administer an available test on the subject, and examine the test results for a significant difference in achievement. The statistical processing of the data is generally highly sophisticated, but the philosophical assumptions that determine the worthiness of either curriculum are neither mentioned nor evaluated.

The question of what is an appropriate education in the sciences is first a philosophical one. The present curriculum reform in science is not simply a change in course content; nothing is gained in biology, for example, if students this year are memorizing the Krebs cycle whereas last year they were memorizing leaf structure, and no amount of testing will answer the question, which is better? It is possible to assess which of several different science courses represents a modern and authentic view of a discipline. In like terms it should not be too difficult to demonstrate whether a course taught for the attainment of concept formation is more useful to a student than one which focuses upon learning definitions and discrete facts. Each of these aspects of the reform can be evaluated, the first by reference to recognized scholars in the subject field, and the second by the capacity of students to go beyond what they learned in class. All of this is to say that a curriculum reform cannot be judged by testing the students' information on science topics.

The goals of the modern science curriculum are longterm and progress toward their achievement is detectable only over a period of several years. This will require the planning of various kinds of longitudinal studies if we are to learn whether the new goals are being reached, whether the new curriculum organization is effective, and the answers to related questions.

When a new curriculum approach is introduced teachers must shift their perceptions, their attitudes toward learning, and their methods of teaching. There is need to recognize a number of unsuspected problems will emerge and immediate solutions will not be available. Students and parents will have doubts, because "things are not like they used to be." School administrators sometimes fail to appreciate the amount of time and effort required of a teacher to change his way of thinking and to effect these changes in the classroom. Guidance and support are essential if the teacher is to be able to make a fair test of new course materials.[19]

The cost of new programs worries school administrators because the assumption is usually made that anything new costs more. For a new school with no equipment it typically costs less to provide the physical resources for teaching the modern curriculum than the traditional. A school well equipped for the old curriculum will need some supplies that are different but not all. New textbooks and laboratory manuals will certainly be needed and whether this is an added expense is a question of where the school stands in the adoption cycle.

SUMMARY

The new directions in the teaching of science represent advances on a broad educational front involving not only the curriculum and its organization, but a change in the entire philosophy about the purposes and values of an education in the sciences. There is a renewed interest in how learning can be improved and made more effective. The need for a clearer theory of instruction has become apparent and there is much discussion about styles and modes for teaching the sciences. New kinds of resource materials have been developed, such as, single concept films, simplified laboratory equipment, tests that require thinking, and booklets on science topics to supplement the textbook and appeal to the special interests of students. Not all aspects of the curriculum reform have progressed at the same rate;

[19] Rowe, Mary Budd, and Hurd, Paul DeHart. "The Use of Inservice Programs to Diagnose Sources of Resistance to Innovation." *Journal of Research in Science Teaching,* 4:3–15, 1966.

the improvement of course content, for example, has moved ahead much faster than the instructional processes required to assure it will be learned satisfactorily. Among the shifting emphases in science teaching over the past decade are the following:

From	*To*
1. Goals defined in personal-social terms;	1. Goals defined in intellectual competency terms;
2. Problem solving as a specified procedure;	2. Modes of inquiry suitable to exploring a discipline;
3. Student-centered curriculum;	3. Disciplined-centered curriculum;
4. Local responsibility for curriculum development guided by high school teachers;	4. National responsibility for curriculum development guided by scientists working with high school teachers;
5. Major emphasis upon informational aspects of science and minimal attention to the processes of science;	5. An emphasis upon science "as a way of knowing," emphasizing the processes of science as they relate to what is known;
6. A survey of many science topics to acquaint students with the range of knowledge in a subject;	6. A few topics explored in depth and taught to the point of understanding;
7. Descriptive and applied science;	7. Interpretive and theoretical science;
8. 'Established' knowledge, with emphasis upon 'basic' facts;	8. Knowledge in the mainstream of modern scientific thinking, with emphasis upon models and theories;
9. Rote learning and memorization;	9. Concept formation and systematic thinking;
10. Group learning, teacher directed, 'telling,' and drill;	10. Individual learning, student centered, guided 'discovery,' and contemplation;

From	*To*
11. The opinion that learning has occurred if information can be repeated;	11. The opinion that learning has occurred if the pupil can use his knowledge in an explanatory or interpretive manner;
12. Subject matter chosen by teachers or textbook authors;	12. Subject matter chosen by research or professional scientists;
13. Personal-social needs of pupils as the criterion base for choosing course content;	13. The conceptual schemes of science as the criterion base for choosing course content;
14. Testing mostly on factual information with a 'right' answer;	14. Testing mostly on the use of concepts to interpret observations or provide explanations;
15. Laboratory exercises to demonstrate, visualize, or verify known information;	15. Laboratory experiments to raise problems, test inquiry skills, and provide 'discovery' opportunities;
16. Laboratory follows class discussion of topics and is largely divorced from classroom learning;	16. Laboratory work as an integral part of class work with pre- and post-laboratory discussion;
17. Learning capability depends almost entirely on student effort and teacher 'telling'; a passive process;	17. Learning capability depends upon organization of curriculum and ability of teacher to match a teaching style with stated goals; an active process;
18. Education focused upon the world as it is today;	18. Education for change and the future;
19. Sequence of learning materials as teacher's arbitrary choice;	19. Sequence of learning materials dependent upon logical structure of discipline;
20. Curriculum improvement through revision and refinement;	20. Curriculum improvement through reform and innovation;
21. Supervision by a curriculum generalist;	21. Supervision by a science specialist;

From	*To*
22. Courses built of instructional units representing a logical organization of information;	22. Courses built around conceptual schemes in a coherent sequence stressing logical unity of discipline;
23. Instruction as information giving;	23. Instruction as information processing;
24. Courses written at a uniform level of conceptualization.	24. Courses written at increasingly higher levels of meaning, building upon previously learned concepts.

Each of the curriculum projects has developed some unique approaches and different kinds of instructional materials which appear to be establishing new directions in teaching. The laboratory block, the single topic film, the filmed experiment, and coordinated supplementary readings are examples.

IV

Concept Learning and the Structure of Science

The modern movement in science curriculum development looks to the nature of science for answers to questions about instructional goals, the design of the curriculum and how science should be taught and learned. We have seen that a scientist is a person who seeks to understand and to explain events found in the natural world. To do so he uses a variety of generalized inquiry procedures in his search for reliable information. He makes observations and tests them through experimentation or by reference to accepted theories. But the information he acquires becomes intellectually useful only when it is brought into a logical organization. When a scientist speaks of the "structure of science" he refers to the conceptual organization of knowledge *and* the inquiry processes giving rise to it; these two phases of science are inseparable. However, in the teaching of school science the emphasis upon 'inquiry processes' and 'knowledge' is seldom equal, nor is the meaning of these terms always in the same sense as used by scientists. The current curriculum reform movement in science teaching is not simply an up dating of course content; it has more to do with the quality of what is taught, with a way of thinking about what is taught and how science should be presented to young people.

The problem in developing science courses is how to communicate an expanding body of scientific knowledge in a way faithful to the discipline and useful to the student. The task is one of converting the more powerful ideas of science into optimal units of instruction which a beginner can learn and which at the same time are meaningful units in terms of science. One means for implementing this idea has been to select a small number of significant conceptual schemes[1] using these to give coherence and unity to a course and then select supporting concepts for each of the schemes. Concepts represent the simplest learning units with meaning in a scientific discipline. A next step is to arrange the concepts to have each concept build upon previous experiences and provide cues for the next order of conceptualization. It should be noted the science curriculum developer has the dual role of selecting sound subject matter in terms of science and at the same time have it pedagogically appropriate.

The choice of conceptual schemes and concepts as a basis for curriculum organization has several advantages. The schemes provide a logical organization to the curriculum and minimize the disconnectedness of the subject matter. The concept provides a teaching module that is practical for pupil learning. This approach has a validity supported by both the structure of scientific knowledge and by modern assumptions about learning. The structure of science was described in a previous chapter and in this chapter we shall examine the nature of concepts and conceptual schemes as they relate to learning science.

THE MEANING OF CONCEPTS

The task of the science teacher is to find ways of making it possible for students to learn science without drowning insight in details, to make knowledge meaningful, to help release students from the confines of current knowledge, and to provide a means for acquiring new knowledge. Achieving these purposes requires examination of the information components describing the curriculum. Traditionally, course guides in science have for the most part been a listing of topics to be taught albeit with some organization. Students are required to learn the planets in order from the distant to the near, the classes of levers, the parts of a leaf, or the physical and chemical properties of oxygen. Lessons are planned somewhat like a shopping list in which items are grouped according to their location in the store. It seems

[1] The characteristics of a conceptual scheme will be explored in some detail later in this chapter. For the time being we can regard conceptual schemes as structural systems in science that accommodate a great many concepts in an organized manner. An example of a conceptual scheme is: Energy is neither created nor destroyed but may be transformed.

apparent very little of the *science* of astronomy, physics, biology or chemistry can be conveyed to students from materials organized in this way. To know the parts of a leaf is not the same as understanding the *complementarity of structure and function;* and to know the number of miles to each planet from the earth does not mean one comprehends *distance. Complementarity* and *distance* are concepts and as such represent a more powerful and economical form of learning than the discrete bits of information forming them.

What is meant by a concept? The term does not have a standard meaning the same for all school subjects, nor do the scientist and psychologist use the term in identical ways. Concepts in science typically describe a more complex kind of organization than a simple response to a class of objects. Concepts differ from facts at one extreme and from theories or conceptual schemes at the other extreme. To form the simplest concept, at least two facts or observations that agree are needed plus at least one more which does not fit into the classification. These facts do not have to be alike but they must form a meaningful unit, or a class of experience, or a common response we can generalize. 'Mammal' is an example of the concept; several facts have been brought into a relationship to convey the idea, 'mammal.' This organization of facts also discriminates between animals that are mammals and animals not mammals. "Living things interact with the total environment" is a concept of a higher order, sometimes called a principle, because a range of conceptual understandings is needed to appreciate the meaning of the statement. In other words, a principle is a matrix of concepts encompassing more information than is found in the mere number of concepts forming the principle.

A concept is a synthesis or logical relationship given to relevant information by the student; it is a product of his own imagination, insight or reasoned judgment. A concept is also more than a collection of organized facts. Facts are essentially bits of information, concepts are mental constructs resulting from the class identity given to the facts by the learner. Facts are available to all who perceive them; they are public property, whereas concepts are a private possession and represent a personal grasp of the relatedness of data. Concepts have a logical structure making the facts within the concepts meaningful and therefore useful in thinking. This means concept formation is something more than simply summarizing, sequencing, or grouping items of information. A concept has a cognitive organization transcending the meaning of its several components. For example, in the concept of 'density' as a ratio of mass to volume, density emerges as a relationship formed by the learner. Essentially density represents a conceptual invention that goes beyond the observed data. When a concept such as density becomes a part of the common experience of people, it acquires a name which makes it possible to share its class identity with others. In this example a numercial expression may be used to more precisely convey its meaning.

Concept is a generic term and it is useful for the purposes of science teaching to consider some of the different kinds of concepts. A concept may be identified as *operational,* representing a way of doing something (determining relative weights); or *classificatory* in the sense of a taxonomy (mammal); or simply *relational* representing a relationship of two or more bits of information (*force* as the product of mass and acceleration). *Affective* concepts are generalized responses described as attitudes, such as, curiosity, excitement, desiring to know, and others. In each of these types, and there are others, isolated observations, actions or an assortment of relevant facts are coded according to whatever properties they may exhibit as a class and at the same time discriminate between classes. We should recognize, however, while all concepts have a class property, different observers may not form identical concepts from the same information. One observer may 'see' an *ameba* as a non-celled animal and someone else sees it as a one-celled organism.

We have not attempted to formulate a precise definition of a concept for to do so would limit its meaning; rather we have sought to develop the 'idea' of a concept. With this idea in mind we can now explore the place of concepts in the learning of science and in curriculum development.

THE PLACE OF FACTS IN SCIENCE

The curriculum reform in science is a major effort to focus teaching upon helping the student develop a representative and significant reservoir of scientific concepts and to minimize the rote memorization of factual information. If this is accomplished then the teaching of science will be more in harmony with the way science is. Facts constitute the findings of a science, they are 'meter readings,' and have little meaning in isolation from other data. They are needed as a basis for concept development and they provide a skeletal framework, but knowing unstructured facts, however many, does not assure their use or value. Explanations in science arise from concepts, theories and principles, and while these explanatory insights arise through a correlation of facts, an explanation of phenomena or events is never found in facts alone. While both facts and concepts are essential for understanding science, teaching limited almost exclusively to the telling, reciting and testing of information does not convey either the meaning or intent of science. To teach only the findings of science is to teach an illusion of scientific knowledge. To be sure one must have an interest in facts since it leads to their discovery, but facts alone are sterile of meaning, unwieldly and uneconomical for teaching purposes. Our responsibility as science teachers is to help young people learn how facts are known and, knowing them, how they can be built from fragments of information into structures having more meaning. It is not our function to educate young people as factual illiterates.

There is an architecture to scientific knowledge, but it is not to be seen in its 'bricks,' however basic these facts may be. While observations and data are basic to science they are neither the means nor the end of science. It is the interaction of theory and logical operations which serves to bring facts together and gives them meaning. Facts become useful and intelligible as parts of verifiable concepts which are in turn illuminated by hypothesis and theories. Concepts and principles, not information, provide the most meaningful units for learning in school for they are a means by which facts and experience can be integrated. Facts outside concepts are blind, concepts without facts are sterile. Facts represent partial answers to problems of the past, but the need in science teaching is for an information organization by which new problems may be met; concepts provide this means since they are generalizable, facts are not. If we expect students to understand the cumulative nature of science it will not be achieved by pyramiding facts, but through understanding how conceptual structures are modified.

HOW CONCEPTS ARE LEARNED

How concepts are learned is basic not only to understanding science but also to the way science is taught. While the research on concept learning provides no well-defined strategy which assures every student will acquire a desired concept, there are considerable data providing cues to the more fruitful instructional practices. Forming a concept is an individual affair and is therefore influenced by the range of characteristics distinguishing one student from another: intellectual capacity, motivation, understanding of the teaching materials, background of relevant concepts and information, and conditions for learning. The way a course is organized and the teacher's mode of instruction will also influence student concept attainment.

A significant factor in developing concepts is the learner's background of experience. Familiarity with a topic is an advantage because it provides a base for incorporating new information. How influential this background knowledge will be depends upon its stability, organization, clarity, meaningfulness and relevancy. In science teaching, concepts related to physical reality and which have substance in direct observation are likely to be easier to acquire than abstract ideas such as mass, evolution, and gravity. Students who know what it means and are aware of how to go about the task of encoding and decoding information are more likely to attain a desired concept than those students without this capability. One of the difficulties in learning the new science curricula is students are *not* taught the intellectual skills important for concept attainment nor are they guided through concept forming processes sufficiently well to know how it is they are expected to learn.

Forming a concept is a searching process, exploring an unordered collection of facts for similarities and differences, for organizational properties and for a meaningful integration. In the process of abstracting a common property from a body of information the student looks for logical relationships, invents constructs and tests them by noting which features characterize most of the data but do not represent other bits of information. The process is one of discriminating, categorizing and evaluating in a cyclic manner, always striving to get a better coding or arrangement of the data. Typically, concept forming proceeds slowly, the concept emerges gradually as information is progressively reorganized. There are times when it may seem to emerge rapidly as in a moment of insight or sudden recognition, but this is usually a terminal response and occurs after one has spent considerable time aggressively searching for identities.

Students are more likely to attain a designated concept if they are exposed to a wide variety of informational stimuli specifically selected for meaningful conceptual properties. Seldom do good concepts result from a 'one shot' teaching activity, a single assignment, or an isolated experiment; what is required is a series of experiences having conceptual relevance. The BSCS Laboratory Block program is a good example of how instructional materials can be logically patterned in a way that, with some promise, most students will achieve the desired concepts.[2]

Concept learning also has characteristics of a decision making process. The learner is presented with an array of facts or conditions and is required: 1) to reduce the differences; 2) to find organizational properties for the information; and then 3) to validate the conceptual organization he gives to the data. Concept learning is not a rote process, the learner is continuously making choices—guessing and testing. After the student selects a strategy for organizing his information he must then ask: is this the only way the data can be related? suppose I change my assumption, is the pattern significant or trivial? is the relationship testable? how appropriate and how adequate is the information I have available? One advantage we have in science teaching is the experimental means by which we can often determine the worthiness of a concept. At other times it may be tested by direct observations in the field, through application in real situations, or by reference to accepted principles, laws, and theories.

Concepts acquire names or symbols making it possible to communicate and share the concept with others, providing they have an appropriate background of related information or experiences. In the upper years of schooling the time required to develop concepts may be shortened through "meaningful verbal learning."[3] This means there must be a minimum level of language skill characteristic of the subject, a reasonable basis of existing knowledge about the topic, an awareness of the relevancy of what is taught to previous knowledge, and an understanding of the associated processes of science. While it is through verbal cues the majority of concepts are attained, we should not forget science concepts are learned, not taught. The student's ability to name or state a concept is not proof of understanding, it may simply represent rote verbal learning. A similar danger exists in attempting to teach a concept by definition or asser-

[2] BSCS. *Laboratory Blocks in Teaching Biology*. Special Publication No. 5. 1967. BSCS. Boulder (Colorado).

[3] Ausubel, David P. *The Psychology of Meaningful Verbal Learning*. 1963. Grune and Stratton, Inc. N.Y.

tion. Definitions in science are an abbreviation or summary statement of a concept symbolizing a relationship of data but not explaining it. To be able to state a definition of gravity or photosynthesis does not imply the learner comprehends the meaning of these terms. Learning a definition without an understanding of the prerequisite facts and concepts is to acquire a fruitless verbalization.

Once a concept is formed by the learner, and depending upon its clarity and adequacy, he is in a fertile position to incorporate new information into the concept with minimal effort. This is one major advantage of conceptualized knowledge; it provides hooks for grasping new knowledge. Then as more information is assimilated the original concept is reorganized, its meaning extended, as well as its discriminatory and predictive powers. The economy of learning concepts results from more coming out than going into the learning; understanding is increased and thought is amplified.

As the student gains experience in forming concepts he increases his competence for doing so. He shifts from strategies with poor results and adopts others seemingly more profitable. A strategy is a search plan for arriving at a goal with a minimum of effort. In learning science it is an informed guess based upon previous experience tempered by a heuristic behavior. In helping a student to learn a concept it is as important to know what strategies he is using to code his data as it is to know the extent of his information. The learning of complex concepts is at times difficult not because of the complexity of the knowledge, but rather the complexities of the logical operations needed to organize the information. This is why a three stage classification system is much more difficult to develop than a one stage although the needed observations are quite simple in either instance.

THE INTERRELATIONSHIP OF CONCEPTS AND CONTEXT

To know a concept implies one is able to go beyond, to infer, to generalize, to make applications, and in other ways extend the interpretive and explanatory uses of knowledge. Much instruction in science courses consists of a single explanation or one example of a topic; this results in concepts not only context bound but limited to a precise situation. Definitions representing concepts also restrict meaning because they separate the concept from relevant principles, laws or theories. For example, diffusion is studied as a phenomenon in biology, in physics, and in chemistry; and in each course it is taught with experiments and examples characteristic only of that subject. This limits the learner's ability to use the concept beyond the situation in which it has been acquired. Thus, he recognizes diffusion as applying only to a specific instance, such as osmosis in plants; and here it may be further bound to what happened to a carrot. Only within this context can the student recognize osmosis and offer an explanation. The range and field of applicability of the concept has been set, in this example, as something characteristic of carrots under certain conditions. The student is not able to explain why an excess of chemical fertilizers on a lawn burns, why the sap in kelp is so viscid, or why salts used as a laxative are potentially dangerous. The power of a concept is increased when teaching has been multi-contextual, that is, when several different instances of diffusion have been presented and the underlying conditions identified. A strong argument for an integrated science curriculum is the convenience it provides for exposing concepts in a wider variety of contexts than is possible in single discipline courses. What we are seeking as science teachers is context-generalizability, a broad frame of reference for the concept, and in this way to make the concept more useful.

Concepts with a single contextual referent are weak, have limited meaning and a short tenure in memory. A well designed science curriculum provides for a number of encounters with the same concept. This is done by revisiting a concept several times in the same course or at different grade levels, but each time in a new context and at a higher order of meaning. Through increasing the range and variety of contexts the meaning of the concept is increased, its potential range of inferences expanded, and the ability to discriminate examplars from non-exemplars refined.

In science the context in which a concept functions influences its meaning and at the same time restricts its range of applicability. For example, the meaning of measurement is dependent upon the context in which the operation of measuring takes place, such as, temperature, length, volume, or time. In addition, each of these measures have variations relative to its appropriateness within a more specific context, for example, length referring to the size of bacteria in contrast to the distance across our galaxy. Time must be considered in reference to an interval to be meaningful, and so must temperature.

Furthermore, we must know the role of time and distance to specify their meaning. It is the restraining action of context which led some psychologists to minimize the extent of transfer in learning. It appears to be more likely as the student gains experience with a concept in varied contexts its transfer potential increases.

Contexts also change, growing or shrinking in meaning as new data, insights, and theories influence the systematic structure of a science. Contrast the interpretations of various life processes in biology today viewed in terms of molecular biology with explanations of a decade or so ago; similarly the concepts of heredity and evolution. The relationship between concepts and context may be viewed as a matrix of interrelated ideas influenced by all the circumstances which disturb the pattern. What a concept in chemistry means in the context of an atomic model serves to define the model as much as to give the relevant concepts meaning. There is an interaction between a concept and the context in which it is learned and in which it functions.

The learning values derived from multicontextual presentations are not the same as having the student repeat, apply or test a concept within a narrow range of situations that serve merely to strengthen what he already knows. While this procedure conserves the original meaning of the concept it restricts its interpretive power. More worthy are activities requiring the student to continually reorganize and re-interpret what he has learned. While simple repetition and contextual variety are both likely to improve retention initially, it is the continuous reorganization of a concept that is most effective for minimizing forgetting. Here again, it is necessary to emphasize that the sequential planning of curriculum materials from grade to grade has much to do with what a student learns and will remember. A good sequence presents a topic in a new context each time it is taught as well as at a higher level of conceptualization.

TEACHING FOR CONCEPT FORMATION

Teaching the new science requires an instructional style supportive of the way students acquire science concepts. Teaching for concept development and the pupil attainment of concepts are interdependent processes. The entire cogency of the new science programs is found in regarding curriculum, teaching strategies, and the learning of science as elements of a unified system. One of the difficulties teachers sometimes experience in using the new science courses is they adopt the textbook but do not adopt the mode of teaching required by the course. The science curriculum reform is as much an effort to modify teaching style as it is the development of new instructional materials. We need to be quite clear at this point; not enough is known about learning and instruction to assume a particular method of teaching will guarantee a specific learning outcome; however, the curriculum and instructional patterns of the new science courses were repeatedly field tested and new insights into teaching have resulted.

The teaching and learning of science courses is unique to the discipline. Science has a conceptual base and it has a structure; these attributes are different from other school subjects and it is reasonable to expect the teaching process will also differ. Charles Eliot, a chemist and a former President of Harvard College, wrote in *Century Magazine,* June, 1884 as follows: "There is very little profit in studying natural science in a book, as if it were grammar or history; for nothing of the peculiar discipline which the proper study of science supplies can be obtained in that way, although some information on scientific subjects may be so acquired." In each of the new science curricular studies there is the implicit assumption that the nature of the discipline prescribes to a large extent the means by which the subject should be taught. This is to say the methodology for teaching science must be closely related to the way science is; its means of inquiry, its structure of knowledge, its theory and models, its logic, and its demands upon data. These characteristics are not the same for descriptive and experimental sciences and the differences are even greater between the natural and behavioral sciences.

Teaching at its best is by design and with purpose. In science courses this means teaching strategies, instructional materials and learning activities need to be specifically correlated with concept assimilation in mind. Basically, the teacher's control over learning is through the inquiry processes and conceptual structure of the discipline. How effective the teacher will be depends in part upon how well *he* has internalized his subject as a science and how well he understands what is involved in teaching for concepts.

The modern science courses are planned in terms of unifying themes which permit a structure of redundancy essential for good concept development. While presently this includes only the arrangement of materials within a particular subject, improvements could be made by extending this relationship between science courses. Ideally, for maximum learning efficiency, a science curriculum should be planned from pre-school through general education in college, with much attention to connections between different subjects. In concept development each relevant learning experience influences the student's approach to the next and the results are cumulative.

A characteristic of the nation-wide curriculum studies has been the effort to build a logical sequence into science courses. What is taught early in the course has meaning for what will be taught later. This requires the textbook to be taught in the order in which it is written, since deviations are likely to damage the student's learning. One reason for the try-out and re-writing of these courses several times was to find appropriate information with a high concept potential and to discover optimal learning sequences. A properly developed course sequence provides a built-in procedure for concept refinement and development. In the teaching of science we are always faced with the problem of a conceptual sequence in harmony with the discipline and at the same time the best suited for learning. The present curriculum reform has contributed greatly to bringing conceptual order to science subjects, but we are less sure they maximize learning. It is reasonable to expect, however, with a coherent organization of subject matter consistent with the discipline, it is likely to be more productive of concept learning than the disconnectedness found in many traditional courses.

It is possible to over-organize a course and thus reduce the potential for concept learning. This may happen when there are not enough learning routes to the concept, the number of relevant instances is too limited, and the levels of meaning too confined to accommodate the range of discriminations needed by students to adequately form the concept. An overload of information will also retard concept formation. Since all students do not learn in the same way a tightly structured course reduces the learning potential of some students. Successful concept formation has as much to do with curriculum organization as with teaching procedures.

A first step in teaching for concept development is to guide the student in acquiring a backlog of basic subject matter, preferably with some logical connections. An orderly arrangement of topics helps to reduce "cognitive strain" and increases the likelihood of concept formation. But merely providing students with large amounts of subject matter is not very helpful unless there is a corresponding richness in concept potential. Instructional materials within a thematic organization are more productive for generating concepts than an array of discrete topics.

Students are more likely to form a desired concept when the teacher employs a wealth of related pathways to this concept, for example, uses carefully selected examples, analogies, illustrations, experiments, demonstrations and concrete experiences conceptually linked. These learning activities need to be presented in the spirit of providing the student with a compass to map his way.

Laboratory experiments, properly planned, provide a particularly favorable avenue to concept attainment; they are concrete, they require the learner to focus his attention on making observations, to convert observations to data, to seek a useful interpretation of the data and to communicate results. But to be the most effective for concept development there must be opportunities for students to try alternative procedures, to devise related experiments, and to choose the means for recording and interpreting their observations. Without this freedom to inquire and to explore on their own, concept attainment may be limited, since each student needs to fit the learning activities into his own cognitive structure and framework of existing knowledge. Extensive reading is helpful for stimulating insight and the formation of concepts. In several of the curriculum studies, notably BSCS, PSSC and Project Physics, supporting reading materials have been developed for this purpose. Audio-visual materials, providing they have a relevant concept identification and are used at the appropriate phase in learning, assist concept learning. In the new science curricula audio-visual materials are designed for use in teaching a specific topic and to serve a special purpose in helping students to conceptualize the information. As we have indicated previously, in teaching for concept development there is always an advantage in having students encounter the concept under as many conditions as feasible and relevant.

A major criticism of much science teaching is the mad pace to cover the textbook by the end of the school year, with the result students are forced to learn by rote, and any concepts acquired are often only shells of verbalism. To merely acquaint students with concepts—a frequent practice—is to limit insight, retention, and usefulness. For good concept development it is essential that science instruction be carefully paced: 1) to reduce guessing and risk taking in forming a concept; 2) to prevent premature closure and as a consequence a weakening of the concept; and 3) to allow time for the student to test his understanding in new contexts. These are among the reasons the developers of the nation-wide curriculum studies sought to reduce the number of major concepts in their courses, thus assuring time for exploring topics in depth and as a result a higher level of pupil understanding. The curriculum question is not depth versus breadth, since in science breadth of meaning and understanding comes only from studying a topic in depth.

Emphasizing positive relationships seems to be more productive for acquiring concepts than stressing negative instances. This does not mean, however, we need to abandon the possibility of illustrating what a concept is by contrasting it with what it is not. Discrimination is basic to concept development and negative factors are sometimes useful for sharpening differences, but there is always the danger the negative instances may be introduced too early—before the student's understanding of the concept has matured sufficiently to distinguish relevant from irrelevant information. Students learn more from positive instances than negative, because they are more willing to work on problems defined positively and prefer positive exemplars to negative.

The question of whether *all* students are capable of conceptualizing is frequently raised. All individuals *do* form concepts and do so years before entering school. Children in the first grade have acquired concepts, and generalize from them; for example, they distinguish dogs from cats, mother from father, moon from sun, automobiles from trains, hot from cold, up from down—each concept representing a class identity apparent to the child. These concepts are, to be sure, limited in meaning, undisciplined, and may sometimes be at odds with accepted scientific interpretations. But it is apparent concept forming is a natural way of learning and can occur without formal instruction. The problem is not whether young people have difficulty forming concepts, but with teaching practices characterized by 'telling,' lack of diversity in assignments, 'one shot' experiments, a compulsion to reach 'closure' with each lesson, too many unrelated facts, and a failure to cluster relevant information; these are the conditions which make it difficult for students to learn concepts.

It is obvious to anyone who has taught science there are apparent differences among students regarding their ability to conceptualize. These differences sometimes result from cultural and educational deprivation. Then again, the difficulty may arise by demanding a level of insight and understanding inconsistent with the instructional materials being used. This would be the case when the material is too unstructured, irrelevant, or there are too many dimensions to the situation. We need to recognize 'readiness' to learn as more a product of appropriate instruction and materials than it is an inherent characteristic of the student. At other times it may be students can find no useful purpose for what is to be learned and none is suggested. Reinforcement for achievement or reward mechanisms may be absent or not apparent to the student. In any case it is only reasonable to expect the reactions to a learning situation will not be the same for every student and all will not progress at the same rate. Concept learning is dependent in part upon the cognitive history of the learner and upon previously assimilated concepts. As students progress in school, these factors magnify differences in achievement.

The teaching of concepts is more successful if the student is familiarized with the content of the concept before formal instruction, in other words, if he knows 'what he is supposed to get out of the lesson.' These may be looked upon as "enticers" which help to motivate the student, or as "advance organizers," such as, conceptual schemes, which help provide a structural basis for new concepts. The learner profits most from an awareness of a rule or principle allowing him to perceive the internal structure of a topic. Teaching for concept development has the form of guiding the pupil. The teacher assists the student to find useful strategies for obtaining relevant information and challenges his ideas. More specifically, he suggests alternate procedures, provides exemplars, recommends readings and experiments, and helps in making responses more precise. He stresses the essential features of the concept by questioning and pointing out interrelations with previously formed concepts. He helps the learner to bring together ideas belonging together and to focus attention upon the relevant variables.

To help assure the highest level of concept attainment within a class requires the presentation of teaching units on several levels of pupil response. The informational response is the lowest level; the chaining of concepts to form principles is a higher level. Much of the criticism of conventional science courses results from the teaching of units all at the same level of knowledge organization.

Teaching for concept attainment by students is greatly influenced by the teacher's conscious effort to stimulate the formation of concepts. He must be continuously aware of the concept sought, its place in a conceptual scheme, and the learning conditions which support concept achievement. Possibly the most important factor of all is that the teacher himself understands and has internalized the concept.

HOW DO WE KNOW A STUDENT HAS LEARNED A CONCEPT?

Frequently we judge whether a student has formed a concept by his ability to verbalize or symbolize it. However, we need to recognize this is not certain proof he understands the concept. We may assume when he is unable to verbalize the concept it still is in an embryo phase; the student expression, "I know it, I just can't say it," is very likely identifying only a partially developed idea. In other words, he cannot act on what he thinks he knows. The student who understands a concept is able to distinguish exemplars from non-exemplars; to interpret new situations using the concept; to use the concept as a hypothesis in problem solving; to make valid inferences or generalizations; to know how to recode new and relevant information; to extract information from the concept and in other ways go beyond the original learning; he 'moves around' in the subject with greater ease and confidence; he appears to learn faster in the topic area. On tests requiring students to reason and interpret novel situations we should expect those who have conceptualized their knowledge to do better. When we speak of an autonomous learner we are describing a student who by the nature of his learning has developed the strategies and concepts which allow him to acquire new knowledge on his own. If the student 'knows' a concept he can extend the range of what he has learned to include related ideas. Possibly the best test of whether a student has internalized a concept is his ability to derive a higher order concept from a subordinate one or to 'chain' concepts in a sequence to form a principle. A simple classroom test of understanding is to have the student explain a concept to someone else.

As we have noted earlier, modern science courses are designed to make use of concepts formed early in the year for developing new concepts and for interpreting related phenomena. This is a major change from a course organization in which each topic is treated once, at which time the teacher 'tells all' he knows about the topic;

and the student, once he has been tested upon the topic, feels he has 'had it.' A close examination of the new science courses will reveal a built-in student evaluation system, one requiring an understanding of one concept before the next in sequence is easily attainable. There is a progressive increase in the level of abstraction and integration as the course continues. The test of a student's understanding is essentially whether he can advance in the course using what he has learned as a nucleus for the next step. When the student feels a course is getting too difficult for him he is quite likely to be reflecting concepts that are ambiguous, or have lost their strength through lack of response. We should also recognize his failure may be due to inadequacies in the course structure, such as, too many unordered facts, failure to cluster relevant concepts, failure to pace needed inquiry processes with subject matter, and failure to build redundancy into the program.

WHAT SCIENCE CONCEPTS SHOULD BE SELECTED FOR TEACHING?

What there is to know in any science is so extensive a lifetime of study is not sufficient to learn all we feel is worthwhile. Science courses, however developed, must of necessity consist of a selection of topics. Any attempt to cover or survey a discipline in 150 to 180 class hours results in a form of superficial learning possessing little interpretive value; this is the meaning of a "watered-down" course, one so diluted with isolated facts its content is intellectually unintelligible. The developers of the new experimental science courses, in seeking to restore rigor, meaning, and conceptual understanding to the curriculum, found in every instance it could only be accomplished by limiting the number of concepts to be learned.

From the time of Herbert Spencer's essay (1859) on "What Knowledge Is Of Most Worth?" the question of what to teach in science courses has been debated. Over the past thirty years an attempt to answer this question, in a presumably objective manner, has been the subject of dozens of doctoral dissertations. Textbooks and courses of study were surveyed and the space devoted to each topic tabulated in some manner leading to a rank order of topics presumed important for teaching. Other investigators have asked scientists, supervisors, teachers, parents, or educators to rate a series of topics they felt should be given priority in curriculum development. Final examinations have been analyzed upon the assumption a teacher tests for those topics he feels most important for students to know and the sum of such topics is a good course. Popularity of topics with students has been another means for selecting what to teach. Common superstitions and misconceptions about science have been collected and the assumption made a good course in science should correct erroneous beliefs. "Persistent human problems" and the "needs" of young people were examined to identify science components for curriculum development. Over the years one finds an increase in statistical refinements (mostly reliability measures) in these studies but no philosophical 'breakthroughs' for selecting curriculum content. Essentially each investigator samples the same curriculum complex and comes out with answers perpetuating traditional topics, albeit in a new order of importance, but never with regard to their significance within the structure of the discipline or in terms of the dependent inquiry processes essential for making the subject matter meaningful. One result is, topics frequently rated high as shown by the survey are viewed as trivial by the scientific community. The cumulative effect over the years has been to establish a major gap between the state of modern scientific knowledge and the subject matter of school science courses.

In the present curriculum reform it was implicitly recognized the content of courses should be limited to topics contributing to the conceptual structure of a science discipline. This means the concepts selected for teaching are authentic and viable in terms of the *science* of biology, physics, geology, and chemistry as the researcher knows them. Whether the concepts meet the personal and social needs of students, or are popular with students and teachers is not the first consideration. The task is to restore intellectual rigor to high school science courses and this is seen as best done within the conceptual framework of the discipline itself. But at the same time it is recognized that conceptual structure is essentially meaningless unless the learner also understands the logical procedures, experimental strategies, and modes of inquiry which help to establish a concept and provide it with status among scientists. Using other criteria as a basis for developing science courses is felt to result in 'un-science' and a curriculum without scientific validity.

Modern science courses are built around conceptual schemes which serve to identify the structure of the discipline and provide criteria for selecting the specific topics to be taught. Essentially these schemes function as threads running throughout the course and provide a means by which the contributing concepts may be ordered. If we regard the conceptual schemes as threads, then concepts represent knots along the way. The concepts selected for teaching are those with the greatest potential for explaining and inferring. The new science courses thus represent a conceptual system with a predesigned set of sequential learning materials serving to give a logical and coherent structure to the course in terms of a particular scientific discipline.

An examination of the various experimental science courses shows some overlap of major science concepts and the inquiry processes. Although fortuitous, it is not surprising, since each discipline can be subsumed under "science" and should therefore reflect the conceptual network and logical methodologies distinguishing science from other disciplines. It is only in this respect the new courses have a curriculum organization. The committees producing the 'new' earth science, biology, physics, and chemistry were directed to "improve" the old courses, which they did; they had no authority to build a high school science curriculum and they did not build one. The selection of concepts for each course might have been different if the vertical organization of the curriculum had been considered.

The implicit criteria for the selection of subject matter to form the new science courses are those suggesting concepts that:

—represent the basic ideas and intellectual structure of the discipline as it is known in modern science
—have the greatest capacity for organizing and explaining the widest variety of phenomena and data
—have the most potential for interpreting, generalizing, and inferring, or in other words those concepts with the greatest logical inclusiveness
—can be taught from a variety of exemplars found in a wide range of contexts
—provide many opportunities for the development of cognitive skills and the logical thought processes which characterize the discipline
—can be used to build other more powerful concepts and principles within science and hopefully provide connections with the conceptual structure of other disciplines
—convey the role of science in man's intellectual achievements.

How many concepts should go into the make-up of a course? This is a difficult number to state, but certainly it should be no more than can be taught to an acceptable level of understanding. The majority of textbooks, modern and conventional, contain too many concepts for the kind of teaching demanded of a conceptually oriented course. The delimiting criteria should be used to select the most representative concepts. A further priority should be given to those concepts which provide a sense of direction within a science and which open the most doors to further learning. Whatever the number of concepts selected, unless sufficient time is taken to develop the concept to the point where the student has intellectual command over it, little has been taught. Progress in learning science is measured in terms of understanding, and not by any number of topics, units, chapters or textbooks covered in one's educational tenure.

HOW CONCEPTS FUNCTION IN LEARNING

The emphasis upon concept formation in modern curriculum theory is derived from the potential which concepts have for improving problem solving and for learning to learn. There would be little use in shifting the focus in science teaching to developing concepts unless it brought about improvements in learning of the kind helpful for realizing the instructional goals of science.

There are a number of advantages to concept learning. A concept provides the best means for getting a lot of information compressed, organized, and into our thinking all at one time. Concepts contain more facts a student can use in a meaningful way, free of the overburden of details, than most other forms of information communication. Learning concepts is one means of reducing the large volume of scientific knowledge available today and simplifying it for use in thinking.

Concepts provide a means for the extension of learning, in other words, to go beyond the initial learning without additional information. As we have seen it is difficult to do much with isolated facts, for example, knowing the normal body temperature of man to be 98.6° F. is not enough information to extend what has been learned. Whereas, understanding the concept of 'warmbloodedness' makes it possible to describe or interpret many things about an animal not yet studied by simply identifying it as warmblooded. This is the difference between knowing an interesting fact and possessing useful information. *Mass* and *heat* as concepts permit the learner to generalize, but if they exist in the student's mind simply as definitions learned by rote they function as facts and have practically no value for problem solving. Knowledge enclosed in a concept raises the generalizability of that knowledge; this means the student is able to generate new meanings and make inferences beyond the specific instances he was taught.

Knowledge acquired as concepts can be used to build more complex concepts, to formulate principles, to bring new information into a logical structure, to define a problem, to generate new ideas, to provide explanations, to make interpretations, to suggest a hypothesis, to direct observations, to organize data, and to make discoveries. How effectively each of these functions can be carried out depends upon conditions such as, how well the student understands the substance of the concept, whether he is aware of its range of application, whether he has a predisposition and the motivation to apply what he knows, and whether he has had experience using concepts to meet new problem situations. While extensions of knowledge are made possible through concepts they do not occur automatically; knowing a concept is one thing, using a concept in a new context is something else. We can be certain, however, that concepts inherently possess meaning for more than one situation and this awareness alone helps the student to notice relevant events and to have some feeling about their plausibility. Forming concepts is one of the best ways we know to have students understand the intellectual power of scientific knowledge. The entire structure of science is dependent upon categories of meaning found within its paradigms, concepts, hypotheses, principles, laws, theories and models. Each of these structures represent a meaningful pattern of information. It is these conceptual systems combined with inquiry processes that make it possible to have the knowledge of science work for us.

Concepts provide knowledge with a predictive element which tells us what to expect under certain conditions or in particular contexts. In this respect a scientific concept and a theory function in about the same way, since they both allow us to make inferences in areas where we have not previously had specific experience.

Laboratory exercises in which students are simply required to record, summarize and report observations are experiments without data. Observations become data when they have been conceptualized through classifying, interrelating, and interpreting. One does not collect data from an experiment; data are made out of the measurements, 'dial readings' or other observations. One function of scientific concepts is to provide the categories into which observations can be fed for coding and possibly turned into data. Without a reservoir of science concepts the student is essentially intellectually helpless in the laboratory, since he either cannot identify relevant observations or provide a means for bringing order to them.

Concepts are remembered much longer than the facts and specific instances of which they are composed. Factors contributing to concept retention are, first, they have a wider range of associations than facts and therefore are used more frequently; and, second, as new bits of information are incorporated, the concept is brought into use and its stability is increased. Remembering is not simply storing a concept in one's mind, nor is it repetitive use; rather it is an integrative process, a continuous reorganization that serves to keep it alive and active. A third reason why concepts are easier to remember is there are fewer of them—they reduce the volume of information and still allow us to engage in all the intellectual activities required by the facts. With the demands on everyone to know more at every phase of life than at any time in past history we cannot afford learning that will soon be forgotten. The value of concept learning is it reduces the necessity for constant relearning. Rotely learned materials tend to remain isolated and thus have a short tenure in memory. Concepts provide a connecting link between work in school and life outside school through their interpretive power and thus are strengthened with use. We have previously stressed the value of a properly sequenced curriculum and the advantage it has for incorporating individual concepts into the structure of a discipline. This also has the advantage of reducing the memory erosion of concepts.

In this section we have illustrated the extent to which the meaning of science is found in concepts generated through intuition and experimentation and at the same time suggested concept attainment as an efficient and effective way of learning. The new science textbooks, in varying degrees, were written to embody concepts in their organization and the authors support a mode of teaching which encourages concept development.

CONCEPTUAL SCHEMES IN SCIENCE CURRICULUM DEVELOPMENT

In each of the experimental science curriculum studies an effort was made to find an organizational basis for the subject matter which would provide an internal logic and a coherent structure for the course. Such a basis would need to have meaning for high school students as well as for scientists. Within the sciences there are unifying "conceptual schemes" serving to integrate the knowledge of the field as well as to provide a focus for scientific investigation. These schemes were identified and used to map out the curriculum territory for each of the new science courses. Not only do the schemes provide a means for organizing a course but they suggest how a student should pattern his learning. Conceptual schemes provide a means for relating the inquiry processes of a science to concepts in a way that nourishes both. For the curriculum developer conceptual schemes provide a means for organizing individual courses as well as the entire science curriculum from the elementary through high school.

THE CHARACTERISTICS OF CONCEPTUAL SCHEMES

There is not a precise definition of a conceptual scheme upon which all scientists agree, but it is possible to describe them.[4] First, they exist in varying degrees of magnitude and complexity. This will be apparent when we examine the conceptual structure of the recent science curriculum developments. At what level the schemes are expressed is an arbitrary decision of the scientist and curriculum developer. Typically they represent a logical relationship among principles or theories, this is to say they are not at the level of simple description or of a concept. For example, when I rub my hands together they get warm, this is a description; numerous observations in different contexts will lead me to recognize friction produces heat; I have now formed a concept. The laws of classical thermodynamics describe a matrix of concepts about heat at a level described as a conceptual scheme. In this sense a conceptual scheme is a network of concepts related in a systematic way; to understand the scheme means not only knowing the component concepts but also their relationship to each other. A conceptual scheme is in no way a collection of concepts; there is a qualitative organization, a totality that represents a cohesion of concepts.

[4] A very readable book which emphasizes conceptual schemes is: J. B. Conant's *On Understanding Science,* Yale University Press, New Haven, 1947. It was published as a Mentor Book (No. MD 68) under the same title, by The New American Library, N.Y.

A conceptual scheme may be thought of as a "society of ideas," forming the theoretical structure of a science. The "interchange of materials and the flow of energy between living things and their environment" is such a scheme. It expresses a system of regularities and uniformities fundamental to understanding biology. As such it has a summarizing function because it incorporates a number of relevant concepts. The scheme explains many things about organisms in relation to their environment; however, the scheme in and of itself does not have an explanation. In the physical sciences, particularly physics and chemistry, the conceptual schemes are expressions of fundamental theories; whereas, in the descriptive sciences, biology and earth science, a scheme is more likely to represent the parameters of a set of interrelated concepts. In both instances the scheme represents the current status of the knowledge within the discipline at its highest level of conceptual organization and in its most stable form. Since conceptual schemes represent a systematic organization of science they also suggest a means for organizing the science curriculum and, as cognitive structures, they have implications for learning.

To this point we have examined conceptual schemes from their substantive dimension. Less well defined, but equally important, are the basic methodological characteristics of science. These are the processes giving rise to the concepts of science and the means by which they are corroborated. They represent the rules used to bring observations into a relationship and an interpretation which we describe as data. To think of the processes of science as conceptual schemes means there are certain skills and values which undergird the scientific enterprise regardless of the discipline. There are always the assumptions: the universe is not capricious; measurement is the means by which assumptions are checked; and the tools of science both determine and limit the nature of our observations. Furthermore, whatever it is that constitutes data in terms of a problem is as much a product of the observer as it is of the observation.

The processes of science or methods of inquiry, as they are sometimes called, are quite similar from one science to another and therefore provide a means by which the various sciences in school may be integrated. In many ways the nature of scientific inquiry is a more effective scheme for curriculum organization than the findings of earth science, biology, chemistry, and physics. Science is distinguished from other subjects in school more by its methodologies than its subject matter and it is just as feasible, and possibly more worthy, to construct the curriculum hierarchy around inquiry processes than upon a pattern of concepts. However, as concepts and processes go hand in hand it is pedagogically sound to plan the systematic organization of the curriculum around both. The creators of the new science courses have recognized the importance of a combined inquiry and conceptual organization, at least to the extent of defining their goals in both these terms.

CONCEPTUAL SCHEMES AND THE NEW SCIENCE CURRICULA

In developing the several courses of the *Biological Sciences Curriculum Study* the authors identified seven conceptual schemes describing modern biological thought and used these to pattern the content of the courses. These schemes are:

—change of living things through time: evolution
—diversity of type and unity of pattern in living things
—the genetic continuity of life
—the complementarity of organism and environment
—the biological roots of behavior
—the complementarity of structure and function
—regulation and homeostasis: preservation of life in the face of change.

By identifying these schemes as representative of biological knowledge in advance of writing it was possible to develop three biology courses for the same student population, with each textbook containing different supporting concepts, but at the same time providing a common insight into the nature of biology.

The *Earth Science Curriculum Project* built their instructional materials around the following subject matter schemes:

—universality of change
—flow of energy in the universe
—adaptation to environmental change
—conservation of mass and energy in the universe
—earth systems in space and time
—uniformitarianism: a key to interpreting the past.

The conceptual schemes of the *Chemical Education Materials Study* are:

—energy and its role in chemical reactions

—conservation of mass-energy in terms of the conservation of atoms and electrical charge
—kinetics and mechanics of chemical reactions
—dynamic equilibria
—competitive factors acting in chemical systems in general
—electron structure and the geometrical arrangement of atoms.

The *Physical Science Study Committee* in developing a high school physics course sought to emphasize the logical unity of physics by stressing the inseparable qualities of *time, space* and *matter*. An understanding of these schemes is built throughout the course by systematically introducing supporting concepts in a logical sequence. Ideas about waves and particles recur throughout the course, each time at a higher level of synthesis absorbing ideas developed earlier into an organization of greater abstraction and thus of greater interpretive value.

In the *Chemical Bond Approach Project* the committee felt there should be one central scheme and chose the study of chemical bonds, "since the making and breaking of these links *is* chemistry." Other schemes used to organize the course are those of energy changes and reaction mechanisms as they relate to chemical systems.

In each of these experimental courses the conceptual schemes provide threads around which a mosaic of related concepts are woven. It is in this way that the modern high school science courses have been able to minimize the piecemeal and fragmentary character of so many traditional courses. This idea has been a major contribution to curriculum development in the sciences. A weakness is found in the failure of some of the projects to identify their schemes more clearly and in the inconsistent manner in which the relevant concepts are fitted into the network. In other cases the conceptual pattern inherent in the course is often too subtle to enable teachers to identify the most useful teaching strategies.

In the field of science there are certain operational schemes characterizing its investigative aspects. In pedagogical terms these are usually identified as inquiry skills or the processes of science. Broadly, these processes represent the intellectual means by which man inquires into nature; that is, organizes his observations, establishes data, focuses it upon a problem and thus seeks to interpret or explain a rational event. This is a phase of science teaching grossly neglected or badly interpreted in conventional science courses. In each of the new science textbooks a special effort is made to shift the content from an expository "rhetoric of conclusions" to a presentation emphasizing science as an intellectual process, and a never-ending quest, emphasizing that whatever is known is tentative and will remain so forever. It is the hope young people will recognize the scientific spirit as a continuing effort to refine and advance science concepts through planned procedures of observation and experimentation, well-seasoned with creative insight and intuition.

The process, inquiry or investigatory schemes are described somewhat differently in each of the new science curriculum projects, but all identify important attributes essential for understanding science. In the *Chemical Education Materials Study* (CHEM) the process schemes are described in terms of student capabilities to be acquired in the course; these are:

—to accumulate information through experimental observations
—to organize information and to observe regularities: to evaluate and interpret data
—to use a model system to account for observed behavior
—to communicate his findings from observations to others
—to appreciate the meaning of uncertainty in science or the absence of certainty
—to recognize that a theory or law need not be correct in every context to be useful in a limited context
—to recognize there is no assurance a law established within a certain range of experience applies outside of this experience
—to understand that the implications of a law (predictions) lead to experiments outside the range of experience upon which the law was based. Interpolation and extrapolation are forms of prediction
—to appreciate that laws in agreement with presently known information may, nevertheless, be changed or abandoned in the future as additional experiments increase our knowledge. Science is not a completed structure but a growing one.
—to make use of scientific activity—observe; find regularity; find explanations (hidden regularities)
—to recognize that science could not advance if our overwhelming mass of knowledge were not ordered with the aid of theories.

In the BSCS courses two major process schemes are identified; science as inquiry and the history of biological conceptions. The latter scheme incorporates two major ideas: 1) the development of biological ideas through time reflecting the fruitfulness of data and the progress made in the development of a particular concept, for example, the continual refinements in the meaning and significance of homeostasis; and 2) the impact of men, events and scientific fashions on achievements in biology; illustrating the ways in which scientific efforts are influenced by chance and intuition. In other words, the logic derived from a mass of data is the logic of the investigator and is restricted by his experience and insight; the processes of science have meaning only within the context of persons, places, time, and the incidents involved.

The inquiry phase of the BSCS is dealt with in a number of ways. The most direct way is through class and laboratory discussions of a number of specially designed "invitations to enquiry." These are lessons designed to involve the student in a dialog leading him to an understanding of some phase of scientific inquiry. The lessons are sequenced so as to make use of answers and insights gained from earlier lessons in combination with a new inquiry. In this way the student learns inquiry is a continuing process with a variety of interacting factors to consider. Each "invitation to enquiry" is in the context of a biological situation allowing the student to sense the relevance of an inquiry process to a problem in biology. The range and sequence of the BSCS inquiry processes are as follows.

I. *Simple inquiry:* The role and nature of general knowledge, data, experiment, control, hypothesis, and problem in scientific investigation.
—interpretation of simple data
—interpretation of variable data
—misinterpretation of data
—interpretation of complex data
—systematic and random error
—planning an experiment
—control of experiment
—"second-best" data
—the problem of sampling
—the idea of hypothesis
—construction of hypotheses
—"if . . . , then . . ." analysis
—practice in hypothesis
—hypothesis: interpretation of abnormality
—origin of scientific problems
—accident in inquiry.

II. *The conception of cause in biological inquiry:* causal factors, multiple causes, time sequences, negative causation, feedback.
—unit causes

—serial causation
—multiple causation
—diverse causation
—diverse effects of diverse causes
—inhibitory causes
—feedback mechanisms.

III. *Quantitative relations in biology:* linear relations, exponential relations, rate, change of rate, units, and constants.
—linear relation
—linearity; limiting factors
—change of rate; complicated variables
—nonlinear polynomial of degree > 1
—nonlinear polynomial of degree < 1
—exponential functions; exponent > 1.[5]

The BSCS staff, recognizing the difficulty with which an understanding of inquiry is acquired by students, developed the concept of the laboratory block designed to engage the student in a substantial biological investigation utilizing a wide range of inquiry skills. Each block represents a biological problem such as, *genetic continuity* or *plant growth* and *development,* and is presented in a way to make the student an independent investigator. One experiment in the block leads to the next, data are accumulated, their limitations identified and as the work in the block progresses the student becomes more and more aware of what it means to inquire into a problem. A block typically lasts for six weeks, ample time to explore the problems of a conceptual system in depth and to acquire something of the meaning of scientific inquiry. Investigative skills are developed and modified as needed to progress on the problem; facts and concepts are brought to bear on the problem when they are useful in helping to answer questions raised by the data.

Time, Space, and Matter . . . investigating the physical world is a secondary school physical science course developed at Princeton University. Here it was the feeling the study of science should provide the student with something more than an account of what is known. It is assumed the student needs to have an opportunity to learn about the physical world through exploring it on his own. The authors feel "the most striking characteristic of this course is its emphasis on the involvement of the student as principal investigator."

[5] The concept of "invitations to enquiry" was developed by Joseph J. Schwab, University of Chicago. The detailed "invitation" for each of the titles listed is found in *Biology Teachers' Handbook,* Biological Sciences Curriculum Study, 1963. John Wiley and Sons, Inc. New York.

The course is built around a series of investigations, from which the student learns to make observations, organize data, interpret results and formulate conclusions. In so doing he acquires the necessary intellectual and laboratory skills as they are needed as well as to recognize the meaning and limitations of what he has learned.

The range of inquiry schemes in *Time, Space and Matter* is extensive and the following are only illustrative:

—simple analogs are useful in studying complex systems
—there is a difference between observation and interpretation
—the strength of a theory depends upon the amount and character of the supporting evidence and on the quality of basic assumptions
—a theory is a tentative answer that cannot be answered by direct observation
—observations can provide tentative answers to questions, but the observation itself may stimulate further questions
—instruments extend the range and character of possible observations
—observations made by the use of an instrument require interpretation
—the use of an instrument may itself introduce some uncertainty in measurement
—observing, questioning, and theorizing are essential to any scientific investigation
—the need for perspective in observation
—the need to examine a situation from various observational levels
—the level of observation and the degree of precision in observation depend upon the purpose at hand; a rough approximation may be appropriate
—several observations may uncover a pattern of change in a situation which may result in a better prediction
—plotting the changing elements in a situation against one another upon a graph
—the arbitrary nature of standard units of measurement
—standards and instruments make it possible to deal quantitatively with observations
—measurement is a process of making successively finer approximations
—there is a limit to the sensitivity, or the response of an instrument
—expressing quantities by scientific notation
—using approximation, precision, and significant figures
—to analyze the validity of a theory in terms of the assumptions which were made initially
—to argue by analogy

—limitations inherent in scaled experiments
—to use a principle, such as superposition, as the guiding proposition of an argument.

The TSM process themes have been presented in some detail to illustrate the range of investigative skills which can be developed in a single course. For each of these skills there is a specifically planned learning sequence involving the student in a 'doing' activity within the subject matter context of the earth sciences. In other words, the student's activity results in forming concepts about the nature of the physical world, about how to study the physical world and in forming an understanding of the interaction of what we know with how we find out.[6]

The *Earth Science Curriculum Project* writing committee wove three major process schemes throughout the ESCP course as follows.

1. *Science as inquiry:* a search for accurate knowledge and a recognition of the incompleteness and uncertainty of present knowledge; unsolved problems; logical and systematic developments of conclusions from accurate observations and well-chosen hypotheses;
2. *Comprehension of scale:* using scales of measurement or units appropriate to the problem; the use of models for the enlargement or reduction of a scale; skill in devising and using models; and intuitive feeling for scale in the real world and in models;
3. *Prediction:* extrapolation from the known to the unknown in either space or time; making logical interpretations of past events from fragmentary records; interpreting past events on the basis of given data.

The laboratory investigations in the course are designed to provide practice in the methods and skills essential to investigating the earth sciences.

The *Chemical Bond Approach Project* seeks to have the student relate conceptual schemes with such process schemes as observation and experimentation. The student collects data but he also applies rules and ideas to these data. Some of the information he needs to solve problems comes from the laboratory and some from the literature; what the student learns is how this information is "fitted into a logical scheme based on a set of assumptions and often some mental

[6] *Time, Space, and Matter . . . investigating the physical world.* Developed by the Secondary School Science Project at Princeton University with the support of the National Science Foundation. Published by Webster Division, McGraw-Hill Book Company, Manchester, Mo. 1966.

model." He learns to recognize how logical reasoning based upon acceptable data may lead to the solution of one problem, but in other instances, will simply identify new difficulties or suggest other questions to be answered. The student learns why investigative skills and quantitative data are important but are not the goals in the search for the solution of a chemical problem. His ability to follow or to construct a line of argument is of more importance.

The *Physical Science Study Committee* in preparing the PSSC physics course emphasized the importance of understanding science as a product of imaginative and creative men and women. They would also have the student recognize how the knowledge of science grows and changes as new insights arise and new questions are asked. Basic laws and theories are at the foundation of modern physics and as such are more likely to be modified than changed; they are, however, not always complete and at times may appear to be in conflict with each other. Physics is dependent upon careful observations and these must always at some stage be transmitted to the mind through our senses. The senses of man need to be augmented by various kinds of tools to increase his range of observations—some as complex as the Stanford University two-mile long linear accelerator and some as simple as a photographic plate. But physics should also teach the limitations of the senses of man as well as of scientific tools. When observations are made it is important to be able to communicate them to others, and mathematics provides a clear and flexible international language of relation and quantity.

In *Project Physics,* a humanistic approach to physics, there is an emphasis upon historical events, persons, and ideas as they have contributed to present knowledge. Laws and theories are frequently treated generally without reference to a specific physical situation. Unique among high school science courses is the emphasis on aspects of the philosophy of science. A supplementary book, the *Physics Reader,* is a collection of articles on what physicists do; the philosophy of science, and the impact of scientific thought on other disciplines. There are articles on "the value of science," "style in science," on "scientific method" by P. W. Bridgman, "merits of the quantitative method," "the nature of science concepts," "failure and success," "the seven false images of science," among others. The range of topics is sufficient to provide the beginning student, should he choose to read each article, with a comprehensive view of what is meant by scientific inquiry.

The Educational Policies Commission in its report on *Education and the Spirit of Science* suggests "rational inquiry" as a major goal of education and as a focus for curriculum development in the sciences. The relevant objectives to be achieved by students are:

—longing to know and understand
—questioning of all things
—search for data and their meaning
—demand for verification
—respect for logic
—consideration of premises
—consideration of consequences.[7]

A coordinated program of science from kindergarten through grade twelve has been recommended by the National Science Teachers Association. One of the ways to integrate the program is a curriculum organization based upon the major processes of science which they have identified as:

—science proceeds on the assumption, based on centuries of experience, that the universe is not capricious
—scientific knowledge is based on observations of samples of matter that are accessible to public investigation in contrast to purely private inspection
—science proceeds in a piecemeal manner, even though it aims at achieving a systematic and comprehensive understanding of various sectors or aspects of nature
—science is not, and will probably never be, a finished enterprise, and there remains very much more to be discovered about how things in the universe behave and how they are interrelated
—measurement is an important feature of most branches of modern science because the formulation as well as the establishment of laws are facilitated through the development of quantitative distinctions.[8]

In *Biological Science: Interaction of Experiments and Ideas,* the BSCS has defined a second level course in biology which is almost entirely a program on the investigative phase of biology. The authors describe the textbook as more *"a guide to learning"* than a book of biological information. The text begins with a description of the nature of science and its meaning for inquiry in biology. There is a

[7] Educational Policies Commission. *Education and the Spirit of Science.* N.E.A., Washington, D.C. 1966.

[8] National Science Teachers Association. *Theory Into Action.* N.E.A., Washington, D.C. 1964.

discussion of biological literature and how to make use of scientific journals and papers. Students learn how to set up hypotheses and to design appropriate experiments; they learn about variables in biological research, and how to measure and to evaluate data statistically. The text contains thirty-eight investigations; some are designed to provide practice in biological techniques and others to test the student's ability to carry out investigations on various biological problems. The book ends with a discussion of science and society and the responsibility of scientists. At the present time this text appears to be the only book at the high school level organized and sequenced entirely upon the investigative schemes of science.

All the textbooks for the new science courses emphasize the inquiry aspects of science by using such phrases as, "we do not know for sure," "the evidence is not complete," "there are two points of view about this," "it is not certain why this happens," "we simply do not know," "this is an unsolved problem," "at this moment we believe," "the evidence is contradictory," and in other ways reflect the status of scientific knowledge. These are all efforts to help prevent the teaching of science as dogma as well as to describe present knowledge within the context of inquiry results.

The laboratory work, about which we will have more to say later, has been developed to be *investigatory* rather than illustrative. The experiment with the potential of an unexpected answer is prized above all others, since it comes nearest to the realities of scientific inquiry.

CONCEPTUAL SCHEMES IN CURRICULUM MAKING

We have shown in some detail how modern science courses are built around a framework of conceptual schemes emphasizing the substantive (conceptual) basis of a science on one hand and its investigative aspects (inquiry) on the other. It is quite apparent these schemes are described in different ways by each curriculum group; however, it is more important to note that in every project there was an effort to develop a conceptual continuity and a systematic relationship between all parts of the course. This is in contrast to many conventional science curricula composed of a series of teaching units each more or less independent of the others. Units or chapters can be assigned in almost any order or even left out without damage to the 'story-line' because the course lacks a logical structure. In the modern science curriculum the developers made a major effort to develop a conceptual interdependence representing a valid picture of the subject. In other words, the course is woven of concepts and conceptual schemes and the result is much like that of a tapestry; an integrated pattern in which any fragment has relevance to the total design. Concepts are not taught in isolation but exist as part of a reference pattern, the conceptual scheme. There is little educational advantage to a hodge-podge of concepts anymore than there is to a hodge-podge of facts.

The use of conceptual schemes in curriculum development has several advantages. They represent the major long-term goals of instruction and help provide the vertical organization of the curriculum, that is, a means for integrating the science of one grade level with another. To an extent these schemes are not entirely the property of any one course (for example, matter-energy relations) therefore they help to provide one means of relating science courses. This procedure for building a curriculum may be one way of reducing the rivalry between special courses and to focus attention on the teaching of *science*.

As a student advances from one science to another, either by grades or subjects, his understanding of a conceptual scheme should take on increasing meaning, in other words, he can explain more phenomena and relate more concepts. This in turn provides us with a means for measuring student progress in science from one year to the next. For example, we should expect students in moving from one science to the next to be increasingly aware of the interdependence of living things and their environment; then at some point when asked to describe the problems man faces in surviving on the moon he can provide an intelligible diagnosis. He should do this better at the end of the twelfth grade than he did in grades ten or six. Relevant knowledge acquired in earth science, biology, chemistry and physics can be brought together because conceptual schemes provide a 'road map' for doing so.

The criteria for the selection of concepts and inquiry skills to be attained in a subject are provided by the conceptual schemes. The question of course content is one of finding supportive learning materials supporting the "design" of the curriculum matrix. The schemes represent a network held together at the nodes by concepts. How effective for learning this organization will be depends not only upon selecting significant concepts but upon their placement and sequence within the curriculum framework. Learning effectiveness is also dependent upon stating conceptual schemes at a level of generalizability that makes them useful for identifying supporting concepts.

Conceptual schemes provide a framework and a map for effective science teaching but do not prescribe the path. Rather they serve as a system through which the natural world is filtered, evaluated and responded to. In another way they assist in making the relevant science facts and concepts noticeable and at the same time provide a means for making them sensible. As integrative threads they facilitate the student's integration of his own learning without forcing a pattern. The conceptual schemes help to keep one from getting lost in a subject, to know when one *is* lost, or to know the road is not a 'through street.'

Conceptual schemes provide, as we have seen, a means for linking concepts within a subject and establishing connections between science and related disciplines. But equally important they provide a tie between the current status of science and future achievements. Two characteristics of conceptual schemes make this possible: 1) they represent the most stable component of scientific knowledge; and 2) they have a cumulative quality, taking on added meaning with new discoveries. Thus a curriculum organization built around conceptual schemes provides a means for incorporating what is new in science and for keeping courses virile. In a more subtle way it is the conceptual schemes that help us recognize what is new and provides the preliminary conditions for thinking about what is new. From another point of view conceptual schemes keep science general, neither bound by time nor localized in content.

CONCEPTUAL SCHEMES AND THE LEARNING OF SCIENCE

In each of the new science curriculum developments there has been some effort to relate course content and its organization to the learning of science. Conceptual schemes, for example, establish the relevance of learning materials and make the task of comprehension easier for the student. They structure the discipline and at the same time provide reference patterns for the student. They grow in meaning for the student as he develops more concepts and gains higher levels of abstraction.

Conceptual schemes are cognitive structures, they exist outside formal scientific proof, they are more implicit than explicit, and represent insights into the organization of science but do not require explanation. They provide not only an organizational pattern for the content of the curriculum, but also define the context in which the learner may most fruitfully focus his learning as he progresses through the curriculum. Since a hierarchal organization characterizes each conceptual scheme, it provides a learning sequence within the curriculum; in other words, the response patterns from today's lesson pave the way for tomorrow's learning. Cues for forming new concepts arise easily from conceptual schemes because there is a symbiotic relationship between concepts and conceptual schemes. As new concepts are formed within the framework of a conceptual scheme, the generalizing potential of the scheme itself is changed making it easier to assimilate more data and increasing its predictability. Whether a subject is "easy" or "hard" to learn is partly related to the extent the material to be learned can be imbedded in a conceptual system. It is easier to assimilate subject material into conceptual schemes for the reason that they have many inbuilt associations which influence insight and meaning.

While science content can be made easier to understand by the proper sequencing of concepts within the conceptual schemes, this does not always mean in a linear fashion. There are times when it is more effective to cluster several concepts so as to build a broader relationship of ideas before going on. We need to remember a conceptual scheme is a *network* of concepts each having some relation to all its components. As teachers we seek to help young people think out these relationships, to find the thematic components and logic holding the subject together. If the student does not begin to "sense" or to internalize the essential organization of a science subject we can expect he will increasingly have difficulty learning it. There is always an internal response in conceptual learning; it is not simply the encoding of new information.

CONCEPTUAL SCHEMES AND TEACHING

Conceptual schemes cannot be taught directly. Concepts and inquiry skills can be taught in reference to schemes, but this is a different matter. It takes years to develop the high order of knowledge represented by a conceptual scheme, it requires a carefully organized curriculum and a mode of teaching that is in harmony with goals of this kind. We have already noted a statement of a scheme does not include its meaning; this is something that grows, develops, and changes with experience. Schemes exist for the student only as he develops an awareness of them, but we may expect a curriculum built around conceptual schemes will have more potential for comprehending them than one that is not. The first steps in developing science courses along these lines is represented by most of the new experimental science projects, however, there is much refinement yet to be done.[9]

[9] As background reading for this chapter from the point of view of learning, see:

Ausubel, D. P. *The Psychology of Meaningful Verbal Learning.* New York: Grune and Stratton, 1963.

Bruner, J. S. *The Process of Education.* Cambridge: Harvard University, 1960.

Gagné, R. M. *The Conditions of Learning.* New York: Holt, Rinehart and Winston, 1965.

V

Problems, Perspectives, and Prospects in Teaching High School Science

The science curriculum reform of the 1960's has brought forth new course materials, defined new goals for instruction, and recommended new styles of teaching. Behind these efforts, however, there continue to exist conflicts about the purposes of science education, disputes about the nature of learning, tensions between curriculum writers and those responsible for educating teachers, and differences of opinion behind the choice of each topic in every course. We have no national policy for American education, no central administration, no official curriculum (the widespread use of a single textbook does, however, represent the unofficial curriculum in a subject), and we have never had a national assessment to determine the over-all quality of science teaching. The situation is one in which we have no immediate means for resolving differences or knowing where we stand in our efforts to improve the science curriculum.

The purpose of this chapter is to identify the strengths and weaknesses of the current reform movement and to examine the major problems and controversies that are in need of further philosophical examination, research, development and testing. It is my purpose to present the debate, the concerns, and emerging reactions that may point directions and define the next steps in the reform movement.

TEN YEARS OF SCIENCE CURRICULUM REFORM: CONTRIBUTIONS AND OMISSIONS

Sufficient time has elapsed to make it possible to note the compelling aspects of the science curriculum reform and to reveal some of its weaknesses. There are aspects of the new curriculum rationale and the instructional materials that are appealing to scientists, educators and teachers, but there are also areas of serious educational concern.

Among the major STRENGTHS of the reform movement that are evident at this time are the following developments:

1. A science curriculum is determined by the state of the knowledge within science disciplines. This establishes the scientific validity of subject matter and provides a sound basis for its continuous revision. Science courses based upon science disciplines provide a pathway of communication between the researcher and the classroom teacher.

2. The content of a science course should consist of modern concepts and principles, organized around the major conceptual schemes that identify a scientific field.

3. Knowledge is an end in itself and learning is its own reward. This presupposes the knowledge is accurate, up-to-date, and contained within a conceptual structure.

4. The meaning and intellectual usefulness of science-based knowledge depends upon understanding the inquiry procedures, the investigatory operations, and the logical processes giving rise to the knowledge.

5. Meaningful learning in science requires the student to participate in the kinds of inquiries characteristic of the scientific enterprise. These may be described loosely as discovery type activities in which the student is more or less autonomous—investigating on his own. The objective is to develop the cognitive or intellectual skills of the learner. This is in contrast to teaching a scientific method based upon a hierarchy of sequential steps from problem to conclusion for the purpose of solving a problem.

6. The satisfactions and aesthetic values from learning science are those of the research scholar. These may be expressed as the joy of discovering and knowing.

7. Knowledge of greatest value in science teaching will in the long run provide the most explanations, the most interpretations, and have the widest generalizing power. This involves understanding the grand principles, the unifying ideas, the symbolic and the abstract attributes of science: for example, organic evolution, entrophy, chemical bonding, and uniformity of earth processes; in other words, the timeless characteristics of scientific knowledge.

8. The curriculum reform has established a better meaning for science through stressing its non-authoritarianism, its intuitiveness, its incertitude, its questions and doubts, its motivations, its dependence upon human qualities, its processes of inquiry, and its unifying principles.

9. The methods of teaching science must complement the nature of scientific knowledge and the means by which this knowledge is attained. Teaching methods are not generalizable beyond the context of the discipline they represent, nor beyond the teacher's comprehension of the subject matter of the discipline and his concept of the scientific enterprise.

10. A science curriculum derived from a discipline and representing its conceptual systems is universal in meaning; it is neither localized nor provincial. This does not mean there is only one way the discipline may be represented in a school curriculum. The four BSCS tenth grade biology courses, the CBA and CHEM Study programs in chemistry, PSSC and *Harvard Project Physics* (HPP), and the two earth science projects, *Time, Space, and Matter* (TSM) and the *Earth Science Curriculum Project* (ESCP), demonstrate how science disciplines may be represented in different ways with each course having universal meaning.

11. A relatively few significant concepts, taught in depth and in context until the student has some intuitive feeling for the topic, is preferable to subject matter "coverage." Breadth of understanding comes through knowing something well and its attainment is demonstrated by the range of explanatory contexts in which a concept can be used.

12. Good teaching is in part dependent upon having available a variety of instructional media to supplement the kind of learning considered desirable for the course. This means the instructional materials must not only be in harmony with the goals of the course but have a definite value for improving the learning of specific topics.

13. The work of the laboratory and field is to provide a means for developing an inquiring mind and generalized methods of problem solving. An experiment is seen as a means for asking questions of nature, and the observations made as a basis for forming data.

14. The new science programs are unique as the only curriculum projects of this century presenting a complete course package, tested, and ready for classroom use. Typically, the package includes a textbook, laboratory manual, teacher's guide or handbook, tests, films

and specially designed laboratory equipment. Each curriculum item is coordinated with and supportive of all other instructional materials. Supplementary pamphlets, laboratory experiments, and reference materials are available, and these, too, are in harmony with the other curriculum items.

Since 1893, beginning with the Committee of Ten,[1] more than forty major efforts have been made to reform the teaching of high school science, but none of these projects had more than a temporary salutary effort on science education. It seems likely this was because the committees recommended new goals and described the course content, usually in outline form, but at no time was the curriculum task carried to the point where it could be used by a classroom teacher without his writing or revising a course of study.

There were other contributions of the reform movement that cannot be defined in terms of specific practices. One of these was the national characteristic of the curricula, aimed at improving American school standards as a whole. The movement raised the academic level of expected achievement for many high school students providing intellectual challenges previously found in only a few high schools. A second achievement was the return of the scientist to the school world as a responsible partner in curriculum development. While he has always had a moral responsibility to communicate the results of his inquiries to others, for the past fifty years he has been satisfied to report to his peers and for the most part neglected the nonprofessional.

Experience with the new science curricula has revealed certain OMISSIONS and WEAKNESSES among which are these:

1. The courses are overly sophisticated and too abstract for the typical high school student. Scientific knowledge can be made simpler and kept accurate without vulgarizing the discipline.

2. Courses are modeled after preprofessional courses with a career orientation and preparation for further study in the subject. They serve more to weed out the nonscientific mind than to provide a general education in the sciences for the greatest number of students. The courses are too closely bound to a scientific discipline neglecting the broader goals of science in contemporary life. All that is offered

[1] National Education Association. U.S. Bureau of Education, *Report of the Committee on Secondary School Studies—Report of the Committee of Ten,* Washington, D.C. National Education Association, 1893.

are the beginnings of a discipline. There is little regard for the need to recast the specialist's knowledge when it is presented to the non-specialist.

3. The courses do not motivate the majority of students toward an interest in science. Among the more frequently cited reasons are: a) lack of apparent relevance to the real world; b) the separation of science from humane and humanistic contexts: c) the personal, the social and the practical applications are missing. The world of the student is a social one, not that of the laboratory. The new courses are not sensitive to the way in which science serves man; their academic formalism overshadows whatever social implications they may contain.

4. Goals of instruction are not stated, or are obscure in their meaning, or when stated, are not reflected in the textbook and related instructional materials. The purposes of laboratory work are the most clearly defined. The concepts to be attained in each chapter are typically not identified nor is their relevance to the pertinent conceptual scheme shown.

5. For each of the new science courses a *Teachers' Guide* or *Handbook* is available, but these contain little information on how science is learned, such as, concept attainment and inquiry development. They focus more on supplementary information for the teacher and answers to questions in the textbook. While alternative content and problems for teaching are described, teaching strategies are not. One result of these omissions is that the modes of teaching are not compatible with the spirit of science or the way young people acquire productive knowledge.

6. The problem of teacher education for the new courses is not solved. Those responsible for the preservice education of science teachers have for the most part not been provided with opportunities to become acquainted with the new programs either in departments of science or of education. Since the projects have not clearly identified the rationale, concepts, inquiry skills, and modes of teaching for the new programs the result is that a majority of in-service science courses are pointless as preparation for teaching them. There is also the faulty, but widely held belief, that improper teaching in high school is corrected by simply knowing more about a subject.

7. Each of the course content improvement projects operated independently of each other in their efforts to develop an improved

science curriculum for the high school. As a result a coherent science curriculum for high schools is lacking because curriculum is something more than a series of courses.

8. With few exceptions (the BSCS special materials and PSSC advanced topics) each new course is confined to a narrow range of student interests and ability. This situation is not an improvement over that of the conventional curriculum.

9. The new science curriculum projects while developed at universities were not a part of the university; therefore, one does not find a cadre of graduate students and curriculum researchers trained to carry on the refinements, evaluations, and associated research essential to the best development of the new courses. It is already evident that the formulators of these courses are becoming conservative in their approach to science teaching. This will be seen in the revised editions of their textbooks. A half decade or more of experience with the courses apparently provided no feedback sufficiently convincing to cause the project directors to modify their original philosophical positions, educational goals, or psychological assumptions. The next steps in science curriculum improvement have not followed the first. A need exists since these courses, especially the physical sciences, have not fulfilled their claims and declining enrollments are apparent.

10. Each of the new courses was designed to fit the existing organization of schools, such as, five class hours per week, one teacher per class, all class periods of equal length, and similar conditions. While the curriculum developers improved what should be learned, they neglected to establish the school organizational conditions under which science could be taught best.

11. There was practically no serious effort to evaluate the learning effectiveness of the new courses in their formative state. While test centers with science observers and teacher feedback sessions were widely used, the information gained was for the most part personal testimony and hard data was lacking. Although the new courses were written to give an elegant picture of the discipline, little attention was given to how the result might appear to students who were studying the material for the first time. There is no system for research and development apparent in the curriculum reform movement.

12. The introduction and diffusion of the new science courses into schools is unplanned and largely mis-directed. More efforts are

made to have the materials reviewed and approved by professional scientific societies than by school agencies. High school teachers are introduced to the materials through departments of science in colleges and universities. Here they are upgraded in course content, and they practice new laboratory techniques, but are not informed about the underlying educational rationale or modes of instruction required to successfully teach the new courses. Curriculum directors, science supervisors, school administrators and those responsible for teacher certification are seldom enlisted in the diffusion process.

13. The new science curriculum does not contain any course inventions that might be described as better meeting the educational requirements of America's scientific-technological-industrialized society with all of its needs for a scientifically literate public. While it was this critical issue that gave rise to these studies. the societal needs were bypassed in favor of professional needs, such as increasing scientific and technical manpower. The opportunity to develop and lend status to general education courses in the sciences was passed, although the directors of several of the projects have published and spoken widely on the need for such an approach.[2] The reputation of a National Science Curriculum Committee tends to make their course recommendations an orthodoxy and it is regrettable they did not use their influence to support the broader educational needs of a science-oriented society.

What the national curriculum committees accomplished was in part restricted by the National Science Foundation, the funding agency for nearly all the projects. Pre-college curriculum development was a new venture for the Foundation and they took a conservative approach to the problem by limiting the work of the committees to "course content improvements." They wished to avoid any suggestion that the Federal Government was interfering with or trying to direct the curricula of the public schools beyond that of reorganizing and updating subject matter. They further cautioned each committee not to put forth a serious effort to influence schools to use the newly developed materials. This directive served to hamper in-service teacher education programs by removing any direct control by the project directors over summer and academic year institutes to retrain science teachers. An interesting situation in this regard emerges from the Federal Government's support on one hand

[2] Bently Glass, Chairman, *Biological Sciences Curriculum Study;* and Glenn Seaborg, Chairman, *Chemical Education Material Study.*

of new curriculum developments, and on the other, of summer- and academic-year programs perpetuating traditional practices. School administrators who release science teachers to obtain preparation for the new programs hear the returning teachers commenting "we didn't learn anything much different from what we have always been doing," and equally often, "what we did learn isn't going to be of much help in high school classes."

Certain limitations and omissions of the science curriculum reform are the result of a lack of policy research preceding the onset of the movement. Policy research has to do with the illumination of issues and long time-projections. It is affected by the conditions under which educational projects are brought into action, decision making processes, monetary funding, and control. There are also basic philosophical questions about which any curriculum developer must be concerned, such as, should science teaching be limited to current and historical concepts of science or do curriculum formulators have some responsibility for shaping the future of society? Do we simply inform students about science and its processes, or focus on productive knowledge and rational thinking? There are other philosophical, psychological, and pedagogical questions to be answered. But since the curriculum reform was initiated at a time of scientific embarrassment (Sputnik), in a period of social and political unrest, and in a furor of educational discontent (typified by public cries for "rigor," "basics," "return to subject matter," down with "life adjustment" and others) the reformers only had time to examine these issues superficially and develop an educationally minimal program. It was not the time to examine the social-historical conditions of a science-oriented culture and to isolate basic assumptions that should underlie a supportive and directive education in the sciences. No policies were established, no continuing research planned, and therefore the next steps in science curriculum development are not apparent.

SCIENCE TEACHING AND THE FUTURE

Science education is a slow-to-react system and there is a considerable time lag between the development of a new curriculum and its diffusion into schools. New science courses require five to ten years to develop and an additional five to ten years before they are used by as many as fifty per cent of the high schools. In other words, this means that for all practical purposes we never have an up-to-date curriculum. Furthermore, even under the best of circumstances, a student rarely gets an education relevant to his lifetime. This suggests that what is needed is an education that more nearly serves the future and extends beyond the context of current information and today's problems. The present reform movement has at best gotten the curriculum up-to-date (at the time of writing) and little more is claimed.

The curriculum problem in science concerns the developing of courses to enable the learner to appreciate the conditions under which he will be living throughout his lifetime. The characteristics of the world in which our students now attend school are not those of the world in which they will earn a living, nor of the world into which they will retire. At no time have they lived in the world of their parents, and the education of their teachers at every level was that of an earlier generation. Science courses are not developed with these concerns in mind, but rely heavily on limited extrapolations from the past. Curriculum planning is shaped by current problems and immediate issues. Next year there will be other pressures to meet, and the following year still others. Pleas for another curriculum revision are made periodically, but for the most part the "new" seldom differs in educational concept or purpose from the preceding. An examination of textbooks or courses of study in biology, physics or chemistry over a fifty-year period will illustrate this point.

Much of what is described as trends in science teaching consists of listing new courses, citing innovative practices, and describing the latest in educational technology and staff organization. These are *not* trends but simply the current state of the art. They represent the fashions and gadgets of the moment, the methods and tools in current use. In school practices we have few educational baselines from which to judge progress, and no stated long-term policies to guide developments. Educational decisions are made at the operational level, almost never at a planning level. Among the results of such action we find: 1) learning is not as efficient as it might be; 2) there is little long-range experimentation and research results are for the most part meaningless; 3) change is slow and conservative, with only an illusion of action created by new educational slogans, hardware, and the further elaboration of specific problems; and 4) the science curriculum young people experience is about a world they will never know—it is of yesteryear, designed to meet the conditions of the moment.

The pace at which technological, social and cultural changes are occurring greatly reduces the relevance of personal experience as a guide to educational judgments. For example, we continue to make decisions assuming an historical continuity without regard to our recent cultural mutation and the technological revolution accompanying it. Herein lies the source of many educational problems that seem so perplexing and confusing. If we seek to plan new directions for science teaching from present conditions, we end where we start; only the problems are new. The alternative is to develop a science curriculum *not* tied to the immediate past, but one relevant to the emerging society and the world that is yet to be. We may not know with certainty the specific conditions young people will face in the future; we do know they will differ from those of today.

The plan of science teaching has typically been to help young people learn a considerable amount about the past and a little of the present achievements in science. This is the easy and convenient thing to do. It rests upon an educational rationale that schools should help young people know and adjust to the societal conditions of the moment. Preparation for life is preparation for the life of today. Education is essentially a form of socialization, a means of absorbing the individual into the on-going activities of the times. To achieve this goal we present a curriculum composed of stable beliefs—at best the information is up-to-date. When gaps or lags are found in the curriculum there is spasmodic excitement to do something to correct the ills; the purpose of the curriculum reform is to ameliorate the ills. Each educational problem is treated as it arises and in isolation from the complexity of forces giving rise to the changing conditions spawning the problems in the first place. Several weaknesses of this approach are: educational issues are dealt with politically rather than through policy and research; and whatever solutions emerge are quite likely to have only a short-range effect. A closer examination of this system will show that it assures its own obsolescence. As the obsolescence becomes apparent there are cries for innovation, experimentation, new instructional tools, and staff reorganization—all as attempts to forestall the waning values of an inappropriate curriculum design.

We are at a time in history where a different view of curriculum planning in science is indicated, just as there is need for new perspectives throughout education. The 'new' we require is a newness of purposes for the teaching of science. It is increasingly apparent from the growing interactions of science and society, science and human values, science and human welfare, science and humanities, science and technology, that the educational demands on schools are those brought about by a society that has changed radically in the past few years and with greater changes to be expected in the next few years. We have a choice to make in education: 1) to be buffeted by the forces of modern society as they emerge, or 2) to develop educational institutions concerned with the designing, molding, and management of the society we desire. There is a difference between adjusting to society and coping with society, between taking society as it is and choosing a future toward which we educate. A student not only needs to learn how the environment affects him, but also how he may affect the environment. This will require a system of education, as seen by John W. Gardner, that provides for a continuous self-renewal of societies and men.[3]

However we view the scientific enterprise it is directed toward change and the refinement of ideas. As the complexity of science increases, so does technology and its potential for influencing the external world. As both forces advance, the rate at which change takes place accelerates and the pattern has been a growing discontinuity between science and society. At times in the past half century there were those who suggested a moratorium on science, so society could 'catch up.' A better solution is to help young people learn how to cope with change, to plan it, and to recognize when change is progress. This will mean orienting science teaching toward the society that could be. The present curriculum is locked into the society that was. In the new curriculum we must look upon science teaching as an agent of change and progress and create ways by which courses can lead in cultural changes and societal development. Our experience has been in designing curricula under the assumption the present is a prologue to the future and any course content changes will require only minor revisions. Our task now becomes one of inventing the future and then planning for its attainment. 'Feed forward' will be more important in our thinking than 'feed back.'

[3] Gardner, John W. *Self-Renewal; the Individual and the Innovative Society*. New York: Harper and Row. 1963.

GOALS FOR THE FUTURE

"Human history becomes more and more a race between education and catastrophe," observed H. G. Wells fifty years ago. To increase the probability of winning this race for mankind we must teach science, and other school subjects, within an education philosophy containing goals that portray the future we seek. This does not mean in some utopian way, but in terms reflecting an educational base for a science oriented culture. The Declaration of Independence is an excellent example of a policy statement describing a way of life different from the past, yet one to which men could aspire in the future. As problems arose and conditions changed, modifications were made in the policy and these are reflected in the amendments to the Constitution. The problems of our society today are not those that can be easily solved by constitutional amendments; on the contrary, they are the sort requiring new perspectives to guide the course of society, to minimize forseeable problems, and to nourish the ideals we seek. A major goal of education will be to help young people recognize and interpret the signals for the future and then behave with intellectual discipline and intellectual competence.

What is worth learning for a period of rapid change and a future only recently designed? First it is necessary to recognize that educational goals map this future as well as provide the educational guidelines for its attainment. They are based upon long-time constant assumptions essential to influencing the direction of science teaching as well as describing what is important to teach. We shall examine some of the conditions and issues underlying the next developments in science teaching, as they appear essential in planning the new reform movement. We shall not attempt to argue the specifics of the next era in science curriculum, but rather present the contexts from which the movement appears to be developing its architecture.

I. Attitudes about Change

Someone described the American temper as one "that is always for progress but seldom for change." The future is not a question of change; the question is the nature of the change. Our task is to develop in young people a favorable attitude toward changes, and to help them develop those that are the most coherent and more productive. This includes an awareness of the processes and rate of change, the multifactedness of contributing forces, and the ecology of change in relation to public policy and social responsibility. The development of this understanding is a part of science teaching because science and technology have become a part of the cultural system and offer a promise that the goals of society may be attainable. But there is little to be gained if we fail to plan the social achievements we desire or to create the intellectual climate essential for their realization. There are other ways in which we must alter our thinking. We can no longer expect that the present contains the educational goals for the future. If we do, we run the risk of becoming a victim of the future rather than an engineer of it. Planning the new curriculum requires us to think of the school as an agent for the realization of social goals rather than limiting it to a process of enculturation. It seems likely we can develop a stronger social commitment on the part of adolescents if we define in a more positive way the goals we seek, the ends to which science can serve mankind.

II. Knowledge for a Changing Society

The knowledge most useful for a world of change needs to have a timeless quality. This is represented by the consolidated knowledge found in the basic concepts, principles, laws, theories, and conceptual schemes of the various sciences. These are the forms of scientific knowledge most generalizable, which allow us to see farther into the future, and which are therefore more likely to be intellectually productive for a changing system. It will be necessary, however, to select topics that are central to achieving specified goals, and most useful for unifying varying systems of thought. We need to be cautious about scientific knowledge at the frontier of science since it is likely to be the most fragmented, the most difficult to communicate to the nonscientist, and to have the fewest applications in the effort to reach social goals. We need to be equally cautious about selecting science topics that are simply congenial with the realities of the moment. New combinations and a greater synthesis of knowledge, integrating the sciences, humanities, and behavioral sciences will be needed for curriculum planning. This is in contrast to the isolation of curriculum components characteristic of the 1958–1970 discipline approach to curriculum development. The knowledge we seek for the science curriculum of the 1980's, 1990's and the Twenty-first Century is to advance the welfare of mankind, and its value is measured in terms of the extent to which it helps realize the goals of education, rather than solves the problems of today or reveals the structure of a discipline for its own sake.

III. Intellectual Skills for the Future

The major intellectual skills needed for a goal oriented society are those characterizing the pursuit of knowledge. To be able to cope with new social problems, new patterns of life, and new styles of personal living requires modes of inquiry and capacities for thinking not now available as outcomes of contemporary science courses. An important concern of education will be to develop skills that provide access to knowledge and its relationships. The student of the future will increasingly need to rely on artificial knowledge aids and intelligence amplifiers, such as, digests, abstracts, mechanical translations, synthesis services, computer classified and summarized data, and new means of information communication. It is already evident we can no longer afford to look up information by means of a card catalog in a library or through guides to the literature. Since knowledge has become a major component of the gross national product, to make knowledge available is a national responsibility; how to take advantage of these services is an educational responsibility. These are some of the intellectual competencies to be acquired through science instruction: 1) the basic tools of logical analysis; 2) proficiency in induction and deduction; 3) the use of models, hypotheses, and theories to organize observations; 4) the use of various systems of thought; 5) ways to assimilate new information; 6) the means of effective communication; 7) how to work with qualitative as well as quantitative data; 8) how to evaluate problems in terms of goals; 9) how to use integrating systems of thought; 10) how to think in terms of policy, in contrast to decision making. Underlying these skills are the attitudes and policies that make their use a disciplined approach to problems involving people.

IV. Careers for the Future

There are new ways in which we must think about science teaching as it contributes to the student's choice of a career in science. In the past, career preparation preceded entrance into a vocation; however, for a period of rapid change special education very likely should be co-existant with experience in a career. This may not be adequate, depending upon the rate of change in science and technology, and it may be necessary to think in terms of career cycles for individuals to forestall their economic devaluation.

V. Summary

The emerging directions for science teaching are based upon new perspectives about curriculum planning. We have not included in previous planning notions of social change, the evolution of scientific and technological knowledge, the interaction of science and society, or a positive orientation of teaching toward educational goals defined in terms of the society we seek or the society in which our students will find themselves living. The new science curriculum designers will need to probe the future to re-assess the current objectives of science teaching, help establish the goals for an organized approach to a specific future, and take leadership in establishing the public educational policies that give direction to a science-based culture. These endeavors alter the character of educational planning as it has been known in the past, and they recognize that educational problems are different from those of the first three quarters of this century. There is an urgency to move forward, for the price of inertia is educational obsolescence and obsolescence is the cause of social and economic disorganization.

PERSPECTIVES AND PROSPECTS

The limitations of the science curriculum reform movement suggest the unresolved problems and something of what needs to be done. In the following sections, some of the major problems and issues will be summarized in terms of the current dialogue. The reader should be aware that scientists and educators write about science teaching from their own preferences and philosophical assumptions both collectively and as individuals. Scientists who reform curricula are concerned with an authentic representation of their discipline and desire nonscientists to appreciate their research. They also hope most people will take advantage of the intellectual processes that characterize scientific study. On the other hand, educators worry more about how the results of scientific investigation may be used for interpreting human experience and understanding the social as well as the natural environment. They are more interested in solving social issues, such as, air pollution, conservation, and food supply, than in problems of solid state physics or getting to the moon. It is not that teachers of science are disinterested in these problems, but they focus more on the welfare of young people and their future achievements than on the fashions of scientific research. These are the two faces of science education, each differing in philosophical assumptions, but not necessarily incompatible. The present curriculum reform efforts have brought about greater mutual understanding of the problems of pre-college science teaching, more than existed a few years ago. However, there has not been enough time, thought, and research to alleviate but a few of the pressures and issues.

It is easier to compare the symptoms and diagnose the ills of science education than to prescribe the needed remedies. But the first steps have been taken, and problems needing further study and research are beginning to emerge.

SCIENCE AND CULTURE

Interpreting human experience requires one to know something of science, which recently has become broadly integrated into the whole of contemporary life. It has not only improved the material conditions of life, but has influenced our modes of thinking in other fields. Science has brought the people of the world together intellectually, but has divided them economically. The history of countries in the world is written today around the scientific and technological revolutions they exert, since these are more important in determining their status and future than political revolutions. The strength of a country lies in its capacity to educate teachers, scientists, and engineers. Scientists are now writing widely on these issues, appraising the role of science in our present culture. No one seems to deny that developing a scientific literacy is an essential component of general education, although there is little agreement as to just what this means. One idea does seem quite clear: the role of science in our culture, its integration into nearly every aspect of human life and human needs, demands a revamping of science teaching to develop a coherence of science and society. The present curriculum reform has resulted in courses that are bound to scientific disciplines neglecting the social aspects of science. Glenn T. Seaborg, Gerald Holton, Frederick Seitz, Richard Meir, Eugene Rabinowitch, Bently Glass, Robert Oppenheimer, I. I. Rabi, J. Bronowski, and many other scientists have written frequently on the importance of relating the teaching of science to its larger human and cultural significance.

Understanding science as a cultural asset, both with reference to its intellectual value and its social import, will require reforming the present science curriculum. New goals are needed and different content is required for courses. If we expect every citizen to be in some degree scientifically literate we must first establish the meaning of this objective. If we expect young people to appreciate those aspects of science which will benefit the future of mankind we must relate natural science to the social and behavioral sciences. This will require that we teach science in a wider context than the processes and concepts of which it is formed. It is essential that the aesthetic and the social values of science be brought out as well as the intellectual. So far philosophy, education, sociology, and the humanities have made no significant contributions toward integrating science into the general framework of human thought and social action, or in helping to close the gap between scientific progress and social adjustment. In part the problem is lack of communication. The science curriculum reformers of the past decade dealt unsuccessfully with social goals and chose to make the curriculum for general education a mirror image of professional education. Children are expected to 'think' like a scientist and to learn science in the way that "provides the scientist with motivation and enthusiasm." But we need to recognize that an education in the sciences becomes science education only in the context of the scientific enterprise, and to appreciate that a general education in the sciences exists only in a social context.

The educational irony of this century would be to alert young people to the great intellectual achievements of science (the nationally developed science courses do this very well), to have them learn about great technological possibilities, to excite them about many achievable innovations, *and then deny these students any insight into the social arrangements which might make such futures real.* Escaping from this paradox requires another round of curriculum development focused on the humanistic, social, political and economic phases of science and technology. Consequently more attention must be given to the values and purposes of science and technology in a modern society. Science as a part of liberal education cannot be taught as an end in itself.

The new reform will demand curriculum teams with special competencies: 1) scientists who can 'unlock' the scientific knowledge found in the thousands of technical journals untranslated for the nonscientists; 2) social scientists who are aware and who understand the social implications of a science-based culture; 3) specialists in science education who can develop the curriculum arrangements required to bring the new information into teachable form; 4) specialists in human learning who are capable of exploring ways in which science knowledge is best acquired and the conditions under which it may be brought into productive use. In contrast to the 1960 reform movement this arrangement of specialists adds more components to the curriculum team, components that are essential to developing the curriculum models suitable for the future.

THE LABORATORY IN SCIENCE INSTRUCTION

"Learning like a scientist," "being a physicist for a day," "the home of a scientist is the laboratory," and "science teaching becomes science through experiments"; these are the phrases used to describe what laboratory work should mean in modern science courses. The decline in the use of experiments for learning began in the 1930's when the lab period was shortened from two hours to one. This was followed by a long series of research studies presumably to show the value of individual experiments for learning science; they did not support the hypothesis. In the period from 1940–1960 the educational concept of the laboratory in general education included the duplication of classical experiments and the visualization of phenomena—somehow these would make science 'real.' During the same period freedom to explore was replaced by specific directions on what to observe, measurements were frequently reported as data or as conclusions, and there was always the 'right' answer to the experiment. The experiment became lost in such teaching mechanisms as activities, things to do, exercises and projects, each of these paralleling specific topics within the course. Students performed according to directions, wrote out answers, and handed them in, but not in the mode of a scientific investigation. Under most circumstances the one thing the student was clearest about when he went into the laboratory was the answer.

At the onset of the reform movement whatever was left of laboratory work had become a performance routine, and science teaching was confined to lectures augmented by charts, films, specimens, models, and displays. It is difficult to identify the combination of conditions that caused this situation. Certainly there were problems of large classes, poor equipment or the lack of it, dissatisfaction with the nature of experiments, class management, short periods, inadequate facilities, but more important, there was a general loss of faith in the learning values derived from laboratory work.[4]

Without exception the science curriculum reform committees believed science could not be taught in an authentic manner unless students were involved in worthwhile experiments. They were not supportive, however, of traditional laboratory practices in high school science courses and felt the need to redefine its purposes, to develop new experiments, and to study the relation of the laboratory to other forms of instruction. While each committee worked on these problems in different ways a consensus is apparent in their thinking. The function of the laboratory is primarily to convey the method and spirit of scientific inquiry. Using the laboratory to collect data by means of prearranged exercises for problems with answers already known, and under conditions in which a divergent answer is always a mistake is to teach un-science. While an experiment is an artificial device to have events happen in ways that may be better observed, the happenings must be characteristic of natural conditions. An experiment is not something apart from nature but a means by which man inquires into nature. The experiment has an important role to play in the process of science, and it is a meaningless activity by itself. The student in the laboratory observes spots, shapes, colors, wavy lines, 'beeps,' movements, dial indicators, structures, phase changes, and many other communications, but this is all they are. To know experimental findings or to collect and display data, however valid, is not enough. The purposes of the laboratory are to involve the learner in the use of logical procedures and strategies, to demonstrate the implications of scientific theories and laws, to pro-

[4] Increasing enrollments, overcrowding of laboratory space, and monetary costs are now causing college science faculty to question the place and educational value of traditional laboratory practices.

vide experience in asking good questions of nature, to provide practice in recognizing regularities, symmetries, diversities, and commonalities among observations. In general, the purpose of the laboratory is to aid the student to impose intellectual order on data, the skills he needs are more intellectual than manipulatory. It was within this rationale that the impetus for the improvement of classroom experiments began.

How have the curriculum reformers sought to improve the laboratory phase of high school science teaching? The following characteristics are representative of the overall movement rather than specific courses and as such can be regarded as current trends to improve laboratory teaching.

I. Goals

1. The use of models, hypotheses, theories, concepts, principles, and laws to direct the search for appropriate observations and to convert observations into data.
2. The choice of appropriate measures to indicate the parameters of data.
3. The appreciation of the relationship between observations and data, data and experimental results, experimental results and interpretations.
4. The coding of obtained observations in terms of the questions to be asked of the data with due regard for variables and degrees of probability.
5. The relationship between experimental options, choice of hypotheses and the meaning of data.
6. The limitations imposed by data on inferences, extrapolations, interpretations, predictions, and generalizations.
7. The characteristics and limitations of experimental designs within and between scientific disciplines.
8. The use of empirical data to form concepts and principles.

These goals for laboratory instruction in the modern science course focus upon the inquiry, discovery, process, or methodological phase of science and upon its intellectual components. This is in contrast to using the laboratory primarily as a place to illustrate, demonstrate, or verify known concepts and laws. The present emphasis upon the investigatory aspects of science is also in contrast to the older goal of problem solving. Now the spirit is more in terms of exploring and coping with problem situations than it is in getting an answer or solving the problem. The laboratory is more a place to develop ideas and raise questions than it is to develop techniques and verify answers. It is not only the problem that is important in an experiment, but equally so the nature of the solving.

II. Laboratory Instruction

1. Class and laboratory activities are mutually supportive and in terms of learning science are not distinguishable from each other.

2. Typically the laboratory begins in the class with a pre-lab discussion of the idea to be explored. Next, observations are made under experimental conditions, followed by a processing of these observations in terms of models, hypotheses, theories or laws. There is a symbiotic relation between the class and laboratory activities.

3. Conveying accurately the investigatory spirit of science requires a continuing series of experiments on the same topic. Each new experiment in the sequence uses the results of previous experiments or adds more information or explores the problem by different means. The laboratory blocks of the BSCS illustrate one development of this idea and the *Time, Space, and Matter* course has a different approach.

4. As the course progresses through the year and the student gains experience in dealing with problems, there is less guidance on how to identify relevant questions and on the techniques for resolving problems. It is expected that the student should become an autonomous learner in the laboratory if his previous experience in the course means anything. In other words, experiments are chosen and placed in a sequence that will move the student along the way to becoming a more effective person as an independent investigator.

5. Work in the laboratory is primarily a way of learning. It is expected that this mode of teaching, in contrast to other procedures, will give the student a better understanding of the conceptual and investigative aspects of science. The present reform has sought to make this statement more generally true than it has been in the past.

III. Characteristics of the Experiment

1. Experiments are chosen for a course to serve specific and definable purposes. Some of these purposes are illustrated by the sec-

tion headed *Goals*. Typically each experiment has knowledge and methodological components and the student is responsible for understanding both.

2. A particular effort has been made in all new courses, biology included, to introduce experiments having a quantitative aspect to the interpretation of results. Where better interpretation of experimental results will be gained there is a pooling of data obtained from different students or groups within the class.

3. While most experiments are based upon an inductive procedure there is a deductive phase in the concept of the 'open-ended' experiment.

4. Considerable effort has gone into the development of simplified equipment for use in experiments. This is not so much a matter of reducing costs as having equipment that will not distract from the expected learning.

5. Filmed experiments from which students make their own observations have been produced by several of the curriculum projects. These films make it possible to have access to costly equipment and complicated set-ups not usually available for high school use.

6. Laboratory manuals have more blank space and the student is encouraged to write the results and interpretation of the experiment as he sees it. The write-up is a measure of the student's capability to reason from observations and not one of his ability to follow directions.

The new movement is directed toward encouraging the use of more laboratory work than has been the traditional practice in high school science courses and improving the quality of the experiments. There is also a recognition that in a high school course it is not possible nor desirable to have all laboratory work at the same level of sophistication. Some laboratory and field activities serve illustrative functions, others represent an investigation, and rarely one may encounter a research oriented experiment. At each level, however, there is an effort to involve the student actively and to have him go beyond the point of gathering simple empirical data.

IV. Perspectives for the Laboratory

The present curriculum reform has brought about a renewed emphasis on the value of the laboratory in science teaching. Certainly the new goals, the fresh experiments, and the suggested modes of teaching are worthy, but the question of what the laboratory can do best is largely unanswered. Especially is this of concern when one views precollege science courses as serving the ends of general education. So far the goals of the laboratory have been those of the professional scientist. They represent the competencies that would advance most anyone who sought a career in the sciences. But the majority of students in high school do not become scientists and less than half find it useful to take as many as two science courses.

What are the legitimate uses of the laboratory for general education? If we consider the optimum conduct of the laboratory and compare it with other ways of learning science what can we expect? The laboratory does not appear to be efficient for rediscovering or exemplifying principles of science. It is also quite likely a student will never use during his lifetime the methods of science embodied in the typical laboratory experiment. The laboratory does, however, provide a form of action that is conducive to learning; it slows down the rate of coverage, rivets attention, and increases the potential for remembering. Of all the skills one might acquire from the laboratory, the one that will serve throughout life is the ability to read science. It is also this activity that consumes more than half of the working time of the professional scientist. Since time is very limited for a high school course it is conceivable that in terms of enduring values a portion of the laboratory time should be used to learn to read in the context of science. This would include aspects of searching the literature; that is, the literature which has been translated from the technical for use by the nonspecialist.

If education is to serve the future, there is likely to be more educational value from laboratory experiments with the objective of developing cognitive skills than there is in collecting data. While the function of the laboratory may continue to be the providing of problem situations, the purpose of these problems needs to be identified in terms of inquiry processes rather than on the more fragile bases of obtaining information and acquiring technical skills. We need to search out experiments that are best calculated to serve as vehicles for understanding, developing, and applying rational processes of inquiry. The range of laboratory problems is the diversity of purposes to be served by the laboratory. One experiment is selected because it can show the influence of conflicting theories on experimental results; a second choice is made because it demonstrates the value of historical developments for interpreting certain observations, and additional experiments provide further insights into how knowledge may be used in seeking explanations and formulating solutions to problems.

The science problems that the precollege student needs to cope with are those of the nonspecialist rather than of the professional. They occur in a societal context, demanding social mechanisms, a knowledge of scientific principles, and the use of rational processes for progress toward their resolution. Problems having to do with maintaining an environment compatible with the welfare of mankind represent one kind of laboratory study suited to phase two of the curriculum reform. The laboratory investigations in today's high school courses are in the context of a discipline and their usefulness is to a large extent confined to the tenure of the course. Those envisaged for tomorrow's science courses are in the context of society and the realness of the problem is the realness of the student's life and his natural environment.

What will the science laboratory be like tomorrow? Different from today's to be sure, and hopefully it will develop the conceptual and intellectual capabilities that find wide application in the *real* world. But it is hardly practical to develop these attributes in science courses without a clear view of the social context in which they will be used.

TEACHING THE NEW SCIENCE

The recent curriculum reform began with criticisms of the way science was being taught. The assumption was made that the teaching of science in schools was dull, uninspired, unimaginative, unscientific, lacking in rigor and organization. The cause of these weaknesses was frequently given as the science 'methods' courses sometimes taken by teachers. While the reformers were deploring 'methods' of teaching on one hand, they developed science courses requiring special teaching methods on the other. In the early phases of each curriculum project teachers were seldom permitted to try out the experimental courses unless they had been to a briefing session, where the new teaching strategies could be learned. Some reformers were hopeful that it might be possible to produce "teacher-proof" materials, so well structured and designed as to make the courses almost impervious to tampering by poorly trained teachers. Even the teacher's task as a motivator of learning was to be taken over by the course of study. The assumption was made that if the course was 'true science' as science is known to the scientist, it would be inherently interesting to young people.

There is little question but that, in spite of their ambivalence, the reformers recognized the need to have their courses taught in special ways if they were to achieve the goals set for them. That they did not give enough attention to this problem is now evident. After a decade of curriculum reform and 'up-grading' of teachers it appears at this time that perhaps as many as two-thirds of the teachers using the textbooks of the new curricula are *not* teaching the course in the mode envisaged by the authors. A large fraction of these teachers know the materials through in-service programs, but they are not certain as to what one does to effect an inquiry, discovery, inductive, process, or investigative teaching style. It is less clear how teaching for concepts differs from teaching for factual information. These new programs demand infinitely skilled teachers using methods of instruction that are supportive of the new goals. And there is little doubt that conventional methods of teaching will not attain these ends. The educational problem is not one of 'methods' or no 'methods' but methods suitable to new goals of instruction, methods that call for teachers to understand the rationale underlying the new courses as well as to know compatible instructional procedures.

Learning psychologists have had no direct part in the development of the new secondary school science courses for they were not invited to participate. Whether they would have made a contribution to the development of the new courses is speculative. Bruner and others have stressed that theories of learning were not what was needed, but theories of instruction. Instruction has to do "with the relationship between how things are presented and how they are learned." What is learned is dependent upon how it is taught and in science teaching the cues for teaching arise from the nature of the discipline. Indirectly, and perhaps to themselves unsuspectedly, the recent curriculum reformers have brought increased attention to the importance of instructional practices in teaching science. This is to say that the successful achievement of the new curriculum goals will be more likely determined by instructional operations than by the content of the curriculum. This is a position similar to the one taken by the Progressive Education Association in the 1930's, by Ralph Tyler in

1950, and more recently by N. Gage, B. O. Smith, J. Bruner and others.[5]

Possibly the most impressive contribution the science curriculum reformers have made to a theory of instruction is their insistence that teaching must have a firm basis in the character of the science disciplines. How science courses should be taught and how teachers should be educated to teach science are crucial issues in the current reform, although the research needed to answer the relevant questions has yet to be done.

The perspectives for the future lie in finding out how science may be learned in terms of the established goals. We need to recognize that some aspects of science are learnable but not teachable, for example, the 'spirit of science,' the worthiness of careful inquiry, and a faith in rational processes. There are different kinds of concepts in science and it is reasonable to expect that they are not all learned in the same way. How the high school science course builds upon the root concepts formed in the elementary school needs careful study. Then there is the problem of how to improve retention in learning. We know very little about the development of autonomous learners or whether it is a realizable goal for very many students. About the only examples we have to study are those we now identify as scholars.

How information in the future is designed, packaged, and communicated will influence the way in which it needs to be taught. Some changes in the mechanisms of instruction have appeared. Team teaching, for example, illustrates a means by which the teachers of a school may cope with the knowledge explosion in science, but it is less clear how this improves pupil learning. Currently there are efforts to develop a 'systems approach' to teaching science. The term tends to be misused and the emphasis is more on hardware than on the nature of learning or the instructional process. There is great need,

[5] The following references will be useful in pursuing the question of instruction:

Bruner, Jerome S. *Toward a Theory of Instruction.* Cambridge: Harvard University Press. 1966.

Gage, N. L. "Toward a Cognitive Theory of Teaching," *Teachers College Record* 65:408–412. (Feb. 1964).

Gage, N. L. "Paradigms for Research on Teaching" in N. L. Gage, ed. *Handbook of Research on Teaching*. American Education Research Association, Chicago: Rand McNally and Company, 1963, Chap. 3.

Smith, B. O. "A Concept of Teaching," *Teachers College Record,* 1960, 61:229–241.

Siegel, Laurence, Ed. *Instruction, Some Contemporary Viewpoints.* San Francisco: Chandler Publishing Co. 1967.

however, to study the problems of human learning, since we can no longer afford the waste of nonproductive teaching.

TRENDS IN CURRICULUM ORGANIZATION

One purpose in developing the new science curriculum has been to create a better sequential organization within courses. Processes of science and conceptual schemes are used to provide a continuity that makes it possible for concepts and inquiry skills formed early in the year to contribute something to the learning which follows. By contrast, the units or chapters of many conventional texts may be taught in most any order the teacher chooses because the inherent logic of a discipline is lacking. To the scientist this means that a valid picture of his subject is destroyed, and to the learning psychologist it is an inefficient way of learning. On the other hand, there are curriculum specialists who feel that the structure of science, as the scientist knows it, is an inappropriate guide for developing high school courses. However, they do recognize the need for students to appreciate the conceptual organization of a subject. The problem is how best to do this, recognizing the intellectual maturity and background of typical high school pupils.

There is the question of whether the same pattern of organization for a given course is suitable for *all* students, the slow, the average, and the gifted learner. A single curriculum is no more suited to the advantaged than it is to the disadvantaged. The BSCS has written a text for the slow learner with content and structural characteristics different from the other three versions for the same age-grade level. The PSSC, CBA, and CHEM courses are written for the top students in high school, since only these students normally take physics or chemistry. One curriculum principle which has emerged from the new science projects is that alternative organizational patterns must be a faithful representation of the discipline and not a substitute for it, such as, a health course for biology or electronics for physics.

Whether science courses should be designed for young people of diverse cultural orientations is debatable. It is important for the purpose of motivation at least to make education relevant to the life situations of students. It is certain with the great variation in the present day high school population, different curriculum organizations are needed and these are not now available. Restructuring of the school day through flexible scheduling and team teaching is one way to modify the instructional program to provide time for working with individuals and small groups in special ways.

There is need for caution in attempting to settle curriculum problems through modifying class schedules and teacher assignments. Consider, for example, flexible scheduling where the size of the large group is 75 to 150 students. One result is that it tends to maximize the range of differences among students. While the research shows students learn as much information from the type of activities—lectures, films, demonstrations—used in classes of 75 to 150 as they do when these activities occur in groups of thirty, the results are less clear for learning concepts. The learning effectiveness in the small groups, two to ten students, in comparison with class sizes of twenty-five to thirty is rarely reported. One is left with the question, until we have more data, as to whether a student who spends part of his time in large class sections and some time in a small group attains the objectives of science teaching more efficiently than with some other type of class organization, for example, an individualized auto-tutorial plan.

What are the perspectives for curriculum organization? The curriculum developers for the 1970's are working on plans to individualize the science curriculum through the use of modular units of instruction. In some instances a computer is used to assist in instruction (CAI) and in other projects to monitor the progress of learning. Each project has its own identifying name and special plans for developing these modules, which essentially consist of a science topic that is logically or conceptionally contained in about five to ten hours of learning time. There may also be several different modules for the same topic, each with a unique approach, for example, extensive directed reading for students who learn easily this way, or an experiment-based approach for those who profit more by 'doing' science. Progress through a module is individually paced. In a year a student would be expected to complete a coordinated series of fifteen to twenty modules representing a subject field such as, physics or chemistry; however, the pattern of modules might be different for each student. The educational endeavor is essentially one of shifting more responsibility for learning to the student. The instructional process is focused upon *learning* activities rather than upon *teaching* activities per se. Supporting visual and auditory learning resources are worked into the instructional system to help assure maximum learning efficiency.

There are fundamental philosophical and learning assumptions underlying the curriculum ventures of the 1970's. One concept is the continuous, vertical organization from the elementary school through the high school. The student progresses from one module to the next in a sequence representing levels of conceptualization. He proceeds at a pace that allows him to master each module before going to the next. Mastery is a measure of achievement in terms of the objectives at some point between 90 to 100 per cent of the criterion measure. Pupil aptitude is defined in terms of the amount of time required to 'master' a module. The quality of instruction in a course is a measure of individual achievements rather than class averages. Curriculum research will in a large measure focus on curriculum arrangements to improve variations in learning. The thrust is to design the information sources in a science course to assure all students will learn. The central problem is how to meet the educational needs of the highly diversified school population we have today. By seeking to individualize instruction and pace learning to each student, we minimize the problems of tracking, failure, grading, testing and motivation we have today. The BSCS with its four versions of tenth grade biology and a choice of approaches in earth science, physics and chemistry provide evidence that diversified courses can be developed in a subject to satisfy common objectives. It appears we now have the conceptual bases to formulate curriculum patterns capable of educating a wider range of pupils than are now being served.

TRENDS IN SCIENCE TEACHER EDUCATION

An experimental course in science carries with it content that is often unfamiliar to many teachers, requires new methodologies, and attempts to achieve new goals. For example, the new courses demand that the teacher's questioning behavior be of a divergent nature rather than of a non-inquiry or convergent type. With the shift of learning responsibilities more to the student and the requirement he should conceptualize and internalize whatever it is he is studying, new demands are upon the student as well as upon the teacher. Teacher education programs in the sciences have not typically been in phase with new high school curriculum developments either in the departments of science or in schools of education.

Several procedures have been used to familiarize teachers with the new curricula, such as, briefing sessions of a few hours or several weeks and the use of local or area consultants. In these sessions the instructor briefly presents the educational rationale of the new program with its methodological demands, describes the course content, and provides an opportunity to work on a typical experiment or two. The National Science Foundation (NSF) has supported over a decade hundreds of summer and academic year institutes for secondary school science teachers at a cost of nearly one-third billion dollars. Typically these programs have been conducted in college or university science departments and are designed to upgrade a teacher's background in science. The topics taught may or may not have relevance to the new curricula projects and when they do, the emphasis is upon recent developments concerning the topic, not how it fits into the conceptual organization of the new course or how it should be taught at the precollege level. The laboratory experiments typically used in the Institute programs are usually from one of the curriculum projects. There is little doubt but that these institutes strengthen the science background of teachers but their total contribution to effective teaching of the new science courses in high schools is disappointing.

Education and science departments have only infrequently restructured their preservice teacher education programs to fit modern science curriculum developments in secondary schools. The reasons for lack of action are different for each of these departments. Science educators and college supervisors of student teachers were very largely left out as participants in the new science curricula developments. The need to develop new kinds of science methods courses for beginning teachers has been recognized but not supported. As a result we find preservice teachers graduating in June and almost immediately applying for an institute program for retraining. On the other hand, science departments do not encourage their best students to go into precollege teaching and see no reason to modify (which should mean *increase*) their course requirements to this end. Thus we find teachers graduating with a major in biology who have never had a course in general biology—one presenting a unified picture of the field—yet this is the only course they are likely ever to teach in high school. Some unidentifiable number of college faculty members are unsympathetic with the new curriculum developments in high school, but not to the extent that they have alternative suggestions. They simply feel that the subject matter is not of the kind they would select, or it duplicates what they are teaching at the college level. Of more serious concern is the college science teacher who fails to identify the difference between an interpreter of science, the high school teacher's major task, and a researcher in science, the function of professional training. The high school science teacher stands between the scientists on one hand and the citizen on the other, and he is the one who has the responsibility for making science meaningful for the man on the street. The problem is that there are practically no science courses designed for his education that enable him to perform the task idealized for him. In probably no other professional field is the educational background so foreign to the performance expectations. The education courses that are required of science teachers tend to be poorly planned, faulty in emphasis, and unnecessarily inconsistent with one another.

If we attempted to identify trends in teacher education that represent the means by which science teachers are prepared to teach the new science courses, we would probably find none. This does not imply one could not find local activities, but there seem to be no serious national efforts which appear fruitful, especially at the preservice level.

The best effort to help in-service teachers use the new science courses effectively is found in the methods books written for each of the courses. There is a *guide* to teaching CHEM study chemistry and one for PSSC physics, a *handbook* for BSCS biology, and a teacher's *manual* exclusively for CBA chemistry. In each of these methods books the goals of the new course are identified, suggestions are made about how to teach the course, background materials and teaching aids are recommended.

The problems and requirements for educating science teachers are surveyed with great frequency, recommendations for a realignment of science and education courses are common, science and education faculty members debate their respective responsibilities, and the result is we enter the 1970's without a program suitable for the education of a modern science teacher. There seems to be little argument about the need of a teacher to be able to conceptualize his teaching field; to understand the relationship of science and society; to appreciate the modes of instruction compatible with the conceptual and investigative phases of a particular science; to know instructional resources and how they may be used to maximize learning; to be able to develop a test and evaluation program consistent with the new goals of instruction; and there are other agreements. But though the problems and issues are recognized, we continue to have no more than a perfunctory preparation for the teaching of science at the pre-college level.

The perspectives for the education of science teachers indicate the desirability of developing within science departments courses or opportunities for those who plan to teach to 1) have a general course or seminar in their major field during their senior year for the purpose of synthesizing the conceptual bases of their major; 2) engage in a substantial research project as a participant or individual worker before receiving their bachelor's degree; 3) have an opportunity to work with materials and to carry out experiments and demonstrations common to high school science programs; 4) become acquainted with the historical, social, political, philosophical and economic aspects of their major field.[6] It is not a question here of the desirability of this work for all science majors, but of indicating it is essential for teachers. The educational foundations for science teachers need to have special relevance for the teaching of science; for example, science teachers need courses in learning which stress concept formation, logical thinking processes, and the development of cognitive skills essential to using the inquiry processes in science. The social foundations courses need to consider the impact of science on the cultural and social history of America. Courses in testing and evaluation should also be relevant to the objectives of science teaching. It is only reasonable to expect that any methods course required of science teachers will include the methods for teaching science. A task analysis of the science teacher's responsibilities will suggest other areas in which he needs preparation.

The traditional in-service program for teachers has usually had something to do with revising the curriculum. Curriculum development on a national basis, using the best scholars and curriculum consultants available, with adequate time and financial resources for the task, has made local developments no longer feasible. In-service education today is more concerned with how new courses can be taught to advantage. This involves questions about the effectiveness of pupil learning and about teacher performance. In-service education is now focused upon instruction and the modification of teaching procedures.

[6] For an elaboration of this point see: Panel on the Preparation of Physics Teachers. *Preparing High School Physics Teachers*. College Park, Maryland: The Commission on College Physics, 1968.

VI

Trends in Evaluation of New Science Curricula

Which of the various national curriculum studies in the sciences are the best? How do they rank in comparison with conventional courses? Are they suitable for most students? These are among the questions teachers, parents, supervisors, and curriculum specialists alike ask about the new science programs. And rightly they should ask. One purpose of this book has been to display the new courses in a way that might suggest answers to some of these questions. On the other hand if one is seeking more precise answers to the questions raised, it is only possible to state that there has been no systematic evaluation of the new secondary school science curricula. This does not mean there has been a lack of evaluative studies, but they have been limited to one facet of a particular course, such as, the 'open-endedness' of laboratory experiments, the teacher's attitude toward the new courses, and most common have been the attempts to compare old and new courses using group test scores. Typically, these studies are inappropriately conceived and their results are not subject to valid interpretations.

There is a certain fondness for describing the worthiness of a new course in terms of its development costs, such as, $7.5 million for PSSC physics, or $9.0 million for the BSCS biology package. At other times the number of textbooks sold the first year, the second year, and so on, is interpreted as an indication of the educational soundness of materials. Whatever value these figures may hold, and others like them, they in no way represent a valid curriculum judgment.

The evaluation issue has always been an important one in curriculum development but seldom has it been dealt with in more than a casual way. The present reform is no exception and what little has been done has come from the inside developers. In the past curriculum changes were slow and the modifications minor, the new was not much different from the old; errors were corrected, units were placed in a different order, pictures were retaken to represent modern dress and scenes, and the preface was rewritten to reflect the popular education slogans of the time. The evolution of the American science textbook flatters the printer more than the authors. The recent curriculum changes, however, are more in terms of a revolution or mutation. They were forced upon the schools by public pressures to improve the "quality" or "excellence" of science teaching, in other words the conventional curriculum was evaluated by the public and judged to be lacking in quality. Something had to be done to improve things. New and unfamiliar authors were financed to write new courses, built upon new goals, organized in terms of a new logic, and taught in the light of learning theories unfamiliar to most teachers. It was these conditions that caused parents, teachers and administrators to become critically aware of the need for some form of evaluation of the new curriculum. The problem of evaluation is complicated by the number of courses available for each subject field; for example, two earth science and other physical science courses that can be taught at the ninth grade; four different BSCS textbooks for the beginning biology course; two major chemistry programs developed under equally responsible authorship (currently one of these, CHEM Study, is available in four versions); and three new approaches to physics teaching. There is also an assortment of curriculum fragments, such as, books of experiments, filmed courses, and other instructional materials. A number of the new developments have educational labels that are not easily understood, such as, process, inquiry, discipline centered, discovery, and creative. The fact these terms are used suggests the new is not like the old, but how it differs is not so clear. The new labels serve more as slogans than as educational practice, and one is hard put to distinguish class performances taught under one label or another. These are the conditions the curriculum evaluator must recognize and it is under these circumstances he must carry out his work. The innovative curricula require new methods of evaluation because the questions to be answered are of a different sort than found in the older programs.

There are several limitations to carrying out the most effective evaluation of the new science curricula. One is we have not identified educational policies or established the educational goals with sufficient clarity and agreement to know what direction a science curriculum should take. Implicit in the new projects is a point of view broadly suggesting what some of these goals might be, such as, education for change, attainment of intellectual skills, and an appreciation of a science-based culture. Not only are the overall purposes of American education obscure, but not all of the science projects are able or willing to identify the specific objectives of their courses in any meaningful way. It is not very helpful for purposes of evaluation to work in terms of "we hope to present physics as physicists know it," although this is what the course is designed to accomplish.

A curriculum evaluation program should not only tell us what is being achieved with science courses but also what meaning this has for the over-all attainment of educational goals. To do this requires we have 'benchmarks' to know where we are making educational progress, where deficiencies lie, and whether the apparent achievements are valid. Evaluation should help us to know the impact a science curriculum has on the educational attainments of people and lead to the improvement of courses. Hopefully, the results of the National Educational Assessment program will provide data that can be used to indicate whether the identifiable goals of the new science curricula are being realized and provide the needed benchmarks. We have sought to point out that curriculum evaluation is something more than counting scores, enrollments, financial costs, and textbook sales. Evaluation is a value-weighted interpretation of goals, objectives, subject matter, teachability and learnability of materials, and costs in time and effort. These are questions that for the most part are independent of students in any direct way. Curriculum evaluation requires judgments of scientists, psychologists, philosophers of science and education, sociologists, and others. It is much more than measuring the extent to which a given program attains the stated objectives in terms of pupil achievement.

COURSE CONTENT VALIDITY

One reason for initiating the recent curriculum reform was to restore the validity of the subject matter in science courses. Scientists examining traditional textbooks and courses of study in their specialty found much of the course content to be something which they did not feel represented their field as they knew it. Typically, the basic concepts and laws of a science were obscured by an overwhelming array of disconnected facts about the subject. They also found the practical applications of science principles and laws were being taught as though they were science concepts. While the textbooks were usually accurate as to facts they were often erroneous in terms of accepted concepts and constructs. At other times the subject matter was either out-of-date or trivial in terms of contemporary scientific thinking. Furthermore, the full meaning of science was not represented, especially its intellectual activities, and its theoretical structures which bring order to a field and provide a unifying picture.

The subject matter validity criterion for the reform movement may be stated as follows: school science courses should accurately reflect the conceptual, investigative and theoretical structure of a discipline and at a point in time as close to the frontier of a field as possible. For some science subjects in high school being up-to-date means a time lag of twenty-five to thirty years in terms of current thinking within the discipline—physics is an example. The content of a biology course might approach on certain topics to within ten to fifteen years of the research frontier. In either case up-to-dateness is defined in terms of understanding the contemporary laws, theories, principles, and experimental operations underlying a scientific discipline.

To assist in restoring content validity to high school science courses, research scientists were selected as directors of the new projects supported by an advisory board or steering committee also composed largely of well-known scientists. Members of these committees were chosen on the basis of their special research interests, professional reputation, and willingness to devote serious attention to the curriculum problems of high school science. High school science subjects are broad field courses representing a large number of research specialities. To be sure of the correctness of each topic area in a course requires the services of many scientists of different research interests. The *Earth Science Curriculum Project* (ESCP) writers, for example, included geologists, oceanographers, meteorologists, geochemists, geographers, geophysicists, soil scientists, and astronomers. More than fifty biological fields are represented in the BSCS courses, and over 1,000 individual scientists were involved in writing or reviewing the course content. Twenty professional biological societies reviewed and commented on the courses after they were written. Over 200 physicists, including several Nobel Laureates, participated at one time or another in writing the PSSC physics course. Other curriculum projects have proceeded in a similar fashion to establish science courses that are authentic in terms of the related discipline.

The use of research scientists as senior authors for developing the new science curriculum is based upon the assumption that those who know science as active researchers are in the best position to recognize what knowledge is significant in a discipline and how it may be given a logical structure. In somewhat more detail, the validity of the subject matter for the new science courses is based upon the following criteria: 1) the basic concepts, laws, and principles as they are currently described provide the topics for a course; 2) the full meaning of the topics is dependent upon having them organized within a structure that typifies the discipline; to understand the parts and not the structure is not to understand science; 3) equal attention is to be given to the investigatory and conceptual phases of science, since they do not exist independently and to separate them is to invalidate the course; 4) the sequence of topics should make it possible to use concepts formed early in a course to help develop new and more abstract concepts later on. The last criterion carries with it the implication that all the chapters or units of a textbook should not be written at the same conceptual level. These criteria also imply the need for continuous changes in the curriculum to keep it up-to-date. Furthermore, they suggest that classroom teachers and local curriculum committees are too isolated from the research frontiers and the new theories in science to function effectively in selecting subject matter that will meet the validity criteria of a discipline. Whether a course meets the demands of the validity criteria rests upon the judgment of qualified scientists.

PEDAGOGICAL VALIDITY

New goals and new course content, especially when the new is more abstract and rigorous than the old, raises questions about how these materials should be taught and how they may best be learned. First, we need to recognize the new courses were not written for *all* students in high school, but were limited by design to a student population identical in number and character found in conventional courses. For example, PSSC physics was planned for students representing about twenty-five per cent of the seniors graduating from high school, whereas Project Physics is for a wider audience. The BSCS range of biology courses was written for eighty per cent of the students enrolled in the tenth grade. The evaluation question is whether the new courses are satisfactorily learned by the students for whom they were designed. Since learning is an active test of teaching, the question might also be phrased: can the new courses be effectively taught? The evaluation question is whether students can master at least ninety per cent of the performances expected when the correct instructional procedures are used. The evaluation measure is the discrepancy between what the course is intended to accomplish and what it does.

Several informal means were used by the curriculum developers to bring the new course content and the teaching and learning performances into line with their identified and implied goals. High school teachers generally known to be excellent classroom teachers of their subject were invited to the curriculum writing centers to help develop the new courses and the supporting instructional materials. They worked closely with the scientists making suggestions about the suitability of the subject matter relative to interest, vocabulary, and reading levels, and whether they felt they could teach the materials effectively. At points of indecision the new subject matter was taught to high school students serving as a test class. Laboratory experiments were tested in the same way to solve such problems as the difficulty of manipulating equipment, understanding the purpose, interpreting results, and completing the experiment in a typical class period. Comments about the experiments were solicited from the students. Following these 'try-outs' the materials were rewritten or redesigned as the need indicated and as time allowed. The logical coherence of the subject matter and the selection of appropriate concepts in terms of the conceptual schemes were the responsibility of the writing scientists.

To determine whether the innovative materials were comprehensible and pedagogically manageable, experimental editions of the textbook, laboratory manual, and sometimes a teacher's guide were printed in a paperback form for classroom testing on a one-year basis in selected schools. These preliminary testing materials were often incomplete in the sense that visuals, review questions and other features of textbooks were only partly developed. Criteria for selecting schools for test centers varied but typically included high schools from which writers for the project had been obtained. This was a distinct advantage because these teachers were in the best position to know the rationale and the hidden goals of the new curriculum. We should recall that most curriculum projects did not start with either a clear-cut rationale or a statement of objectives. These evolved as the writers debated what the new course should be like or what the inadequacies of the traditional courses were. All teachers participating in a trial year were required to have a one- or two-week briefing session before teaching the new materials. The experimental teachers at the test centers were experienced in teaching their subject, had a strong background of academic preparation in the required science, and were considered by their school administrators to be effective teachers. Every effort was made to keep the experimental high school classes 'typical' of the regular enrollment for the particular science and school. In other words, the plan for evaluating each new course was to involve 'expert' teachers with 'normal' classes.

As the experimental classes were taught the project headquarters staff was provided with feedback on how things were going. Pupil difficulties in understanding the text material and unsatisfactory experiments received most of the attention. Suggestions for improving sections of the course were solicited from trial teachers and special feedback forms were filled in weekly. Teachers were also requested to keep a daily log of their reactions to the course. At more or less regular intervals the experimental teachers from a test center or geographical region were brought together for a lengthy discussion of their reactions to the curriculum materials as they were being developed. These meetings were also attended by one or more college scientists and at least one member from the staff of the project. These sessions provided a consensus reaction to the new courses and gave the observers a feeling for what needed to be done with the courses at the next rewriting sessions.

There were at least two points of view held by the curriculum developers about the quantity of feedback essential to improving the course under development. The Physical Science Study Committee (PSSC), Chemical Bond Approach (CBA), and Project Physics (PP) used a small number of carefully selected schools and teachers. With a small number of teachers they felt a closer liaison could be maintained between the evaluators and writers of the new program. Most project directors found that useful feedback comes from only a comparatively few teachers and their critical comments show a high degree of consistency. It thus appeared logical to confine the testing of a new program to a minimum number of schools.

The first version of the Earth Science Curriculum Project (ESCP) textbook was tested by seventy-seven teachers and 14,000 students. These numbers were increased for the second and third trial years. The Chemical Education Material Study (CHEM) was tested for three years and in the final year 560 teachers and 45,000 students were involved. The schools were located in forty-six states. The Biological Sciences Curriculum Study (BSCS) began its testing program with 100 teachers, grouped into fifteen test centers located in thirteen states, involving nearly 15,000 students. The following year, 1961–62, thirty-six test centers were established, twelve for each of the three text versions. At this time 500 high schools participated and 50,000 pupils. Along with the schools in the test centers there was always a limited number of independent teachers granted permission to use the materials in return for feedback. By the time the three text versions were ready for the final revision they had been taught to over 80,000 students and rewritten three times. The BSCS regarded the test centers not only as a source of feedback on the courses, but as a means of in-service education for teachers. At the time the BSCS texts were published more than 1,000 biology teachers had had experience in teaching one or more versions.

The BSCS *Special Materials* course was written to accommodate the particular problems of the unsuccessful learner in high school biology. An unsuccessful learner was defined as one falling below the fortieth percentile on the *Differential Aptitude Test* and essentially failing in his school work. Since the BSCS wished to prepare a valid biology course for this particular segment of the school population the test classes were selected on the basis of specific criteria. A year was used to study these young people to get ideas about how to develop the course in a way that would be educationally sound, that is, motivating, understandable, and properly paced. The teachers involved in the first trial year were experienced in working with slow learners and sympathetic with their problems. Preliminary course materials were taught to selected classes of these pupils; a total of thirty-two schools and 1,000 students were involved. On the basis of feedback from these teachers the materials were revised and rewritten and in the second trial year 300 teachers and 16,000 students made up the test sample. This led to a further refinement of the 'special materials' before publication.

Is the *new* science curriculum pedagogically valid? This is certain to evoke the question as to whether the *old* curriculum was ever valid or did it attain its position because of a venerable history? However one examines this question it is certain that at no other time in the history of science teaching has so much effort been made to determine the educational validity of science courses. To be certain, there are philosophical weaknesses in these evaluative procedures. Much of the data assembled and used to make major curriculum decisions would ordinarily never be acceptable in any context of scientific or educational research. Data gathering was naive by research standards and its interpretation was outside of any educational theory that might give direction to its meaning. On the other hand, there is little doubt but that the new science curricula are more like science than conventional courses. Course structures are certainly more logical than in traditional programs; whether the arrangement improves student learning is not so clear. It appears the conditions for learning were taken for granted by the curriculum innovators.

The problems of determining the pedagogical validity of a curriculum are many, and perhaps we do not possess all the technical means for carrying out the task. It is better, however, that we recognize what some of these problems are. Certainly one problem is the weaknesses of feedback as a source of reliable data. Although the feedback comes from the consumer of a program this in no way assures its usefulness for developing a new curriculum. In at least one of the new curriculum studies, if all the feedback had been taken seriously by the developers, the experimental course would have been programed back to the traditional. This came about by teachers commenting: "this will be a good course if you include these topics." "These topics" were almost always those of the old curriculum and furthermore they were the most traditional. Very little of the feedback had to do with the conceptual structure of the course, its goals, or operations for effective teaching. The teachers were not trained as participant-observers in an experimental situation and under these circumstances there is a tendency to report annoyances as difficulties and to react negatively to topics which are not understood. When project directors find feedback contrary to their expectations their reaction is to question the validity of the judgment. Nevertheless, reactions from hundreds of teachers working with thousands of students over a three- or four-year period is of some positive value. The information obtained did serve to improve the reading level of the texts; the feasibility of teaching certain topics was determined; the quality of experiments was improved; it was found pupils could learn more rigorous material than had been previously suspected; and it was found possible to teach the inquiry procedures of a scientific discipline. Feedback is, nevertheless, a form of personal testimony and however detailed does not in itself constitute a reliable evaluation. Questions may be raised but seldom are answers obtained. Those providing feedback are constrained by their knowledge of curriculum theory and by their understanding of what is meant by effective learning.

The present science teaching reform is an instructional-curriculum package. The mode of teaching is inseparably bound to the content of the curriculum in much the same way the processes are related to the products of science. This is the reason the curriculum developers did not want teachers to try the new courses until they had been informed about the style of teaching that would be required. Unfortunately the various institute programs for teachers, except usually those briefing sessions supervised by a project's staff, neglected to emphasize how the knowledge of a discipline is effectively communicated. It was assumed that quality of instruction is exclusively a product of what the teacher knows rather than of what the student learns. On the basis of this assumption, as we have pointed out previously, the improvement of teaching is seen only as a by-product of upgrading the teacher's knowledge of science. There is a curious disregard in attempting to judge the effectiveness of a new curriculum. So little is said about the effect of optimal learning conditions and the quality of instruction. It is not truly possible to evaluate a science curriculum without considering the nature of the teaching as well as the kind of learning that is expected. Quality of teaching is closely correlated with the educational achievement of students, more so than with the specific subject matter that is taught. Although more than a decade has passed since the new science program was introduced into schools we still lack evidence about its educational effectiveness.

A few of the problems that need to be considered in an evaluation program to determine the pedagogical validity of a course are:

1. Can the material be learned in the way defined by the rationale

and goals and learned by all pupils? What alternative approaches may be needed to reach everyone? Part of the answers to these questions may lie in the organization, sequencing, and pacing of the instructional materials.

2. What is the quality of instruction required to teach the course in terms of the restrictions set by the rationale, goals, and objectives? This is not only a question of the management of learning but also of the academic and professional qualifications of the teacher. What will be the cost if the teacher needs to be retrained and the instructional program reorganized? The final judgment as to cost is defined in terms of pupil achievements generated by a program. Cost is a measure of what and how long it takes for a student to master a course. It should be noted that references to the quality of instruction are in terms of what pupils learn as individuals rather than as a class or group.

3. Teaching is something more than communicating the content of a textbook and laboratory guide. Does the material interest and motivate students to self-sustained learning? Are there attributes both in the teaching of the class and in the instructional materials which will provide reinforcement for learning? Some of the new science curricula appear to be so context bound within the discipline that students are unable to find any relevance for human experience, and as a result soon lose interest in the subject. A successful course is one in which students can learn, want to learn, and seek to use what they have learned. All the new science curricula assume a transfer of methods and scientific principles; this suggests the value of a particular learning is found in relevant transfer and in the generalizability of knowledge.

There may be a concern about the difficulty of assessing some of the variables indicated in these questions, but this in no way negates the responsibility for evaluating the pedagogical validity of a new curriculum.

SOCIAL AND PHILOSOPHICAL VALIDITY

There is a tendency for curriculum evaluators to consider only those objectives of a course which are internal to a science discipline. Thus we find evaluation confined to the student's knowledge about the subject and his ability to solve problems and to recognize worthy experimental procedures. Long-range goals of the program are not examined and neither are the connections between science and other phases of the total high school curriculum. One major criticism of the national agencies on course development is that they are not integrated or related to each other in any very clear way. Each group has worked independently of the other not only within the sciences, but between science and other subjects.

Are the students who have had two or three courses of the new science and an equal number of the new mathematics any more analytical or rational in their thinking than students who have had only the old program? Do students taking the new sciences behave differently in other school subjects, such as, social studies, senior problems, and English? Do the new courses represent a new curriculum in science or simply a series of new courses? These and similar questions are a part of curriculum evaluation, though they have not been so in the past. Without answers to these questions, however fuzzy they may be, there is no way to judge the soundness of a curriculum innovation.

Science is taught because it is expected to do something for individuals living in a particular society and at a time represented by the cultural context. Curricula are planned in terms of society and one goal is the development of socially responsible people. It is imperative for a science-based culture to have a school program oriented to developing scientifically literate people capable of advancing the society of which they are a part. The main elements of education and social policy are not separate. This means instruction in science should have real-life values. A discipline bound science curriculum may be too restricted to help young people deal with problems requiring an understanding of the interaction of science and society. Social realities produce social problems, which are always problems of education and, increasingly so, problems of science. Problems of over-population, world food supply, racial understandings, scientific and technical manpower, conservation of space, air pollution, ecological displacement, and similar problems are not to be solved without some understanding of science. But on the other hand they are not likely to be solved at the scientist's bench or in the field without relevance to mankind and a feeling about human values. The high school with a socially valid curriculum in the sciences has the means to educate toward the solution of problems that bridge science and society. A science curriculum without this potential and without these goals serves vocational and professional ends, and not those of general education.

A valid science curriculum is not only up-to-date in terms of science, but also in terms of relevant social issues. What a science course should teach is the interpenetration and connections between science and other achievements of human beings to the end that it helps us understand our times and leads to social betterment. General education in the sciences at the high school level can exist only in a social context if the purposes of secondary education are to be achieved.

It is not possible to evaluate a school curriculum and not evaluate its goals. There is more to educational evaluation than finding whether the stated goals are being achieved by the subject matter selected and the teaching operations prescribed. Goals can be contradictory to the social good, they can be trivial in terms of contemporary living, and they can be shortsighted. It is in this last condition, shortsightedness, that we are likely to find the greatest weakness in educational goals. Educational goals define the life we want; they express our aspirations as well as provide educational directions. This suggests schools have a responsibility for helping to plan social change to assure the future environments we seek. Education is thus an agency of social engineering and a primary force for shaping the future. It is not sufficient to acquaint young people with the achievements and promises of a science-based culture, while denying them any insight into the arrangements needed to cope with this society for realizing the best in human potential and welfare. The serious curriculum evaluator cannot avoid these value judgments and at the same time hope to assess the impact of new science courses.

SUMMARY

We have attempted to show that one does not evaluate a curriculum by comparing one course with another to learn whether it is better or worse on some measure. From the modern point of view evaluation is concerned with determining the validities of a course and its potential impact upon the individual and society. It is not alone a matter of evaluating the new in terms of current practices but also in terms of the futures we seek. It is essential to look at the school in terms of a long-range planning system and at the curriculum as an instrument for individual and social development—not as an end in itself. When a school program is evaluated we cannot avoid judgments about its relevance to a changing world, to human aspirations, and to societal plans for the future. A basic problem of evaluation is that of determining in what ways new teaching materials and ideas can be used and the limits within which they are effective. Whatever we lack in evaluative theory and techniques to carry out a modern program of evaluation requires in itself innovation and invention.

VII

Curriculum Models for Teaching Secondary School Science

This chapter describes curriculum projects representative of the science reform movement during the past decade. Only those studies developed for nation-wide use, and which meet at least several of the evaluation criteria outlined previously are included. Thus each course was evolved experimentally in the sense it was written to bring a new approach to teaching a science, tested in a number of high schools by qualified teachers, rewritten and retested with a new sample of students until such time the developers felt fairly certain they had an effective program. Only studies representing a complete one-year course for high school are reported. During the reform movement a number of curriculum fragments were written consisting of one or two units of instruction, a new set of laboratory experiments and demonstrations on a topic that might be useful in a course, films and slides on special science topics but independent of a particular curriculum, and projects limited to improving or inventing new apparatus were carried out. These materials will not be described although many are valuable contributions to science teaching.

Official documents, newsletters, research reports, and personal interviews were used as the reference source for all statements about the curriculum studies reported here. The interpretations of these documents are those of the author and he alone is responsible. The author, a science curriculum specialist, has been on the staff and a consultant to several of the projects reported. An extensive bibliography on the studies reported is found at the end of this chapter.

EARTH SCIENCE COURSES

I. Time, Space, and Matter

The *Secondary School Science Project,* also known as the Princeton Project and by the course title *Time, Space, and Matter* (TSM), is an interrelated series of investigations of the physical world. The course was developed at Princeton University in the department of geology but with the collaboration of chemists and physicists. The course is designed for use at several grade levels in secondary schools, although it is most widely used at the ninth grade.

Time, Space, and Matter (TSM) is based on the assumption science teaching should focus on the inquiry processes of science, offering the student not only an account of what has been discovered but a systematic and logical method of thinking. Thus the emphasis in the course is one of having students actively investigate aspects of the physical world. The concepts developed in TSM are basic to understanding chemistry, physics, mathematics, astronomy, and geology; these are *time, space,* and *matter.* While topics about the earth are used as the vehicle for the development of these concepts, TSM is not intended to be an earth science course as such. The developers use the earth and its materials because they provide a tangible means by which students can learn from their own observations and make a systematic study of the physical world. The learning emphasis is on 'guided discovery,' utilizing structured investigations to optimize the opportunities for discovering relationships. At stated intervals students organize and apply what they have learned—this is in contrast to the usual use of review questions.

A major objective of the course is to provide opportunities for students to observe, record, analyze, and formulate inferences from data. From these activities it is the expectation students will be both motivated and capable of thinking about problems of the physical world in a more analytical way.

Time, Space, and Matter was first tested in grades five through nine during the 1962–63 school year. The potentialities of the project were evident and the materials were rewritten and expanded during the summer of 1963. Preparation was also begun on a number of supplementary materials for the teacher's use. The course was tested a second time during the 1964–65 school year at fifty-six schools in eight cities. The final version of TSM was published in

1966 by the Webster Division of the McGraw-Hill Book Company.

The plan of the course is a series of investigations conceptually and logically related to each other and building toward a climax of ideas. As a student proceeds with an investigation, he records his observations, hypotheses, speculations, and conclusions. These notes comprise the basic content of the course since there is no formal textbook. In essence the student writes his own text. The investigations are carried out in the spirit of an inquiry emphasizing the discovery of relationships. The needed skills of instrumentation and measurement are developed within the context of each investigation. Constant use is made of mathematics to help uncover quantitative relationships and to illustrate the importance of precise expression.

The course is organized into three major divisions. The first division, *On the Nature of Things,* is a series of investigations focusing on observation skills, methods for quantifying data, and such inquiry processes as inferring and theorizing. The conceptual content material is selected from physics. The second division, *Seeking Regularity in Matter,* shifts the orientation from physics to chemistry, and the student studies the occurrence and behavior of matter. *Interpreting a World of Change* is the theme for a third series of investigations. Here the student uses the 'stuff' of the earth and from it develops hypotheses about the composition of the earth and forces producing change. The student uses his concepts drawn from physics and chemistry to complement the principles derived from geology. The sequencing of these three major series of investigations is planned to lead the student from observations of the concrete in the first series to the abstract in the second and back to the concrete in the third.

Series I, *On the Nature of Things,* is composed of nine investigations. The first one, "Encountering the Physical World," raises the question of how to study the physical world. Subsequent investigations develop the student's power of observation and emphasize precision in verbal description as well as in mathematics. Investigation nine, "Worlds in Space," provides an opportunity for the student to apply his skills and information obtained in prior activities to a study of the sun. To date only the series *On the Nature of Things* has been published; *Seeking Regularity in Matter,* and *Interpreting a World of Change* are not available.

The style of teaching required for TSM is one based upon a structured-discovery approach. This does not imply the student is set adrift, but rather he is placed in situations designed to optimize discovery and to provide him with the skills for doing so. Perhaps the most striking characteristic of TSM is the emphasis on active participation in learning in contrast to the traditional passivity of the learner. The student manipulates materials, measures, observes, speculates, interprets, and extrapolates. He discovers information for himself rather than having it passed on to him from an external source. The sequencing of the materials requires students to continually apply and refine skills and concepts learned in previous investigations. New investigations build on the information and skills achieved in prior ones. The teacher is an active participant in the investigations. He suggests experiments and judges when to introduce new learning materials. He stimulates students through questions that may lead to answers, he organizes discussions, and serves as a guide to learning.

There is a *Teacher's Folio* for each investigation providing background information on the problems encountered by the students in the *Student Investigation Booklets.* The folio describes the observations the students should be making and the concepts they should form during the investigation. Questions are suggested for use at the end of each phase of an investigation to help the student check out his knowledge and to evaluate his own performance and understanding.

The TSM program consists of a variety of instructional materials which include the following types of items:

Student Investigation Booklets provide the student with photographic observations to supplement those he makes in the laboratory. These booklets are not textbooks but sources of data from which interpretations can be made. The observations from the photographs are those the pupil could not directly make for himself. Continuity is provided by the brief text at the beginning of each booklet and captions accompanying the pictures. Titles for investigations one through nine are: *Encountering the Physical World; Exploring a Slice of the Earth; From Microcosm to Macrocosm; Levels of Approximation; Dimensions of the Earth; The Surface of the Earth; The Grand Canyon of the Colorado; The Surface of the Moon;* and *Worlds in Space.*

The Science Reading Series consists of short paperback booklets designed to help dramatize the relationship between the microcosm of the laboratory and the macrocosm of the physical world. Some of the titles of the reading series are: *The Story of Project Apollo; The*

Lunar "First"; Down the Colorado!; On a Piece of Chalk; A Night To Remember; and *Conquering the Matterhorn.*

The Student Record Book contains blank pages on which the student records his observations and interpretations as he progresses through an investigation.

The Student Laboratory Kit consists of an inexpensive book-sized box of simple equipment that can easily be carried home to continue investigations started in the classroom. The laboratory materials required for the course are for the most part familiar items, rocks, clay, ice, and salt.

A *Teacher Folio* accompanies each student booklet and provides background information and practical suggestions for the work of the student.

Time, Space, and Matter: A New Approach to Secondary School Science is an overview book describing the objectives, rationale, content, and structure of the course and the sequence of the investigations.

Tests and examinations, 16 mm. films, film loops, and additional teacher aids for TSM are being developed.

II. Earth Science Curriculum Project (ESCP)

The *Earth Science Curriculum Project* is an interdisciplinary approach to investigating the earth. It incorporates information from the sciences of astronomy, geology, meteorology, oceanography and physical geography.

The administrative control of the ESCP is under the American Geological Institute. Its financial support is from the National Science Foundation. The planning and development of the curriculum materials has been guided by an interdisciplinary committee of scientists and educators appointed through the American Geological Institute. The planning, writing, and testing of curriculum materials began in 1962. The course materials have been written primarily for use in the ninth grade. This decision was based upon a 1963 ESCP survey of the status of earth science offerings in schools.

The curriculum developers felt the ESCP course should represent the unity of the earth sciences. This is in contrast to a course composed of special units on astronomy, geology, meteorology, oceanography, soil science and physical geography. The ESCP introduces a considerable amount of biology, physics, chemistry, and mathematics into the course. Concepts from these fields are considered basic to an understanding of the forces and processes affecting rocks, land masses, the oceans, the atmosphere, and the earth in space.

The ESCP course is one of the first major efforts to present a unified or integrated science course representing several disciplines focused upon logically related scientific principles. The unifying themes for the course are: 1) the study of man's environment; and 2) earth science as a process of inquiry. There is an effort to convey to pupils the investigative nature of science as a search for new and more accurate knowledge about the earth. To achieve these goals the curriculum planners have selected text material and laboratory investigations stressing, for example, the notion of time, the incompleteness of evidence, the difficulties of experimental verification, and the necessity for tentative and speculative conclusions. The unsolved problems of earth science are identified and the student learns to appreciate that whatever is known in science today is simply the current status of knowledge.

The development of the *Earth Science Curriculum Project* is similar to that of other national curriculum studies in science. In this instance a professional society, the American Geological Institute, through its Steering Committee, outlined the unifying themes of an earth science course. A writing team of twenty earth scientists and classroom teachers prepared the first experimental course including a textbook, laboratory manual and teacher's guide. This course was taught in fifteen test centers during the 1964–65 school year. Approximately 7,500 students and seventy-seven teachers were involved in the first trials. Based upon feedback from the first experimental year a revised edition was published in 1965. This edition of *Investigating the Earth* was taught to 10,000 students in seventy-five schools during the 1965–66 school year. A final revision based on the 1966 testing was published by Houghton Mifflin Company in 1967. A significant change in the final revision of the course materials was the elimination of the laboratory manual. All laboratory investigations are now included in appropriate sections of the text in an effort to more effectively have the laboratory become an important source of information in the course.

The conceptual themes used in organizing the subject matter center around the water cycle and rock cycle. Some of these themes are: universality of change, flow of energy in the universe, adjustment to environmental change, conservation of mass and energy, earth systems in space and time, and uniformity of process. One historical theme stresses the quest for knowledge as a human endeavor. The inquiry theme includes: understanding scale, models, prediction, uncertainty, and related skills and attitudes.

Investigating the Earth is divided into four major units with twenty-six supporting chapters. The first unit treats the earth as a dynamic system. Unit two explores the cyclic nature of earth processes. The earth as a historical record is developed in unit three and the last unit is a study of the relationship of the earth to the universe.

Laboratory investigations and activities are in the textbook and are part of the chapter organization. In some instances an investigation is the student's first encounter with a particular concept. In other situations the laboratory provides for the application and refinement of a concept.

The ESCP is an activity-centered program. Students need the freedom and encouragement to investigate and speculate on their own. Laboratory investigations are for the most part open-ended and allow for multiple working hypotheses. The teaching style required to attain the course objectives is one that sustains inquiry by encouraging students to question, to explain, to extrapolate, and to speculate as the problem requires.

The *Teacher's Guide* lists the major ideas and behavioral objectives for each chapter in addition to suggesting a time schedule and identifying a teaching approach. Materials presented in the student's textbook are explained in detail in a corresponding chapter of the teacher's guide. Laboratory investigations are described in detail and a time schedule for the prelab-lab-postlab sequence is suggested. Acceptable answers to problems and thought questions, evaluation suggestions, references, and audio-visual aids are also listed. Forty-one overhead transparency masters are included in the appendix of the guide.

The instructional materials currently available for the ESCP course are: *Investigating the Earth.* Houghton-Mifflin Co., Boston. 1967 (a student text); and *Teacher's Guide,* Vol. I and II. Houghton-Mifflin Co., Boston. 1967.

Also available is a *Reference Series,* published by Prentice-Hall, Inc., N. J. It is composed of single pamphlets on: *Sources of Earth Science Information: Selected References for Earth Science Courses; Selected Earth Science Films; Selected Maps and Earth Science Publications; Free Materials for Earth Science Teachers; Planetariums,*

Observatories, and Earth Science Exhibits; Topographic Maps: Their Use and Interpretation; Basic Data and Water Budget Computation for Selected Cities in North America; Selected Guides for Geological Field Study in Canada and the United States; others in progress.

ESCP Laboratory Kits, complete sets of ESCP apparatus and materials needed to conduct primary and optional investigations, can be purchased from science supply houses. The equipment and materials are for the most part not expendable and will require replacement only as the result of normal usage or breakage.

Two *ESCP tests* are available from *The Psychological Corporation,* New York. They are: *Test of Science Knowledge: Part I—Factual Information;* 2) *Test of Science Knowledge: Part II—Principles.*

ESCP Films, produced especially for ESCP in 16 mm. by the Encyclopaedia Britannica Educational Corporation, Chicago. *Toward Inquiry* is a teacher education film and *How Solid Is a Rock?* is the first in a series of ESCP content films. One feature of this film is the provision for stoppage at certain intervals to provide for analysis and questions by students.

The ESCP project has a *Newsletter* and a *Teacher Information Bulletin.* A *Field Study Guide Series* and a series of *Single Topic* films are being developed.

PHYSICAL SCIENCE

An alternative to earth science as a ninth grade offering is a course in physical science. One is *Introductory Physical Science* (IPS) developed by the IPS Group of Educational Services Incorporated and published in 1967 by Prentice-Hall, Incorporated. This is a year-long course designed to provide beginning students with some insight into how scientific knowledge is acquired as well as a background of physical principles.

The course was developed by a group of scientists and science teachers under the direction of Uri Haber-Schaim, a physicist on the staff of Educational Services Incorporated of Watertown, Massachusetts. This is the organization responsible for the PSSC course in physics, the first of the experimental projects in the curriculum reform movement. Planning for this course began after the work of PSSC, CBA, CHEM, and the BSCS and at a time when it was becoming apparent to the teachers of these courses that high school students typically were deficient in basic science skills and lacked an understanding of the meaning of science. More specifically, it was found senior high school students in the new science curricula were: 1) inexperienced in making observations; 2) lacking basic laboratory skills; 3) unable to apply elementary mathematics to experimental results; 4) incapable of correlating an abstract idea with a concrete situation; 5) unfamiliar with orders of magnitude; 6) unable to judge what is important and what is not; 7) without a feeling for approximation; and 8) convinced science had little meaning for real life or for anything they could do. The rationale for the IPS course is primarily one of correcting the intellectual ills of students in high school science courses, particularly in physics and chemistry. The IPS committee is persuaded the course is also desirable for students who do not intend to take a physical science in high school. For students planning to take more science IPS is most appropriately placed in grade nine or eight. A few schools have taught the course in grade eleven or twelve for students not planning additional work in science. There are no prerequisities for IPS.

The goals for IPS are: 1) to develop a feeling for the kind of human effort involved in the development of science; 2) to have students recognize that the root of all science is in the exploration of natural phenomena; 3) to provide experience in scientific investigation; 4) to learn how, where appropriate, to generalize from observation; 5) to understand how to construct models or theories which can be manipulated logically and which may serve to raise new questions; and 6) to recognize the advantages and limitations of laboratory experiment. The specific objectives of the course are reflected in the rationale leading to its development.

The development of a curriculum to realize the stated goals and objectives began in 1963. In 1963–64, ten teachers tested the program under classroom conditions. These teachers had for the most part been involved in developing the class and laboratory materials. The feedback from this trial was encouraging and in 1964–65, sixty teachers taught the course to 2,300 students. The student population was increased to 25,000 in 1965–66 and in 1966–67 to 100,000 students distributed throughout forty-seven states and six foreign countries. The final commercial version of the program was published in 1967.

The content of the course provides a unified picture of the atomic model of matter in all the variations and contexts the model implies. Topics were selected by applying the following criteria: 1) will a topic be useful at several points in the course? 2) what will the student benefit by learning the topic? and 3) is the topic essential for developing the story-line of the course? Care was used to select learning materials that were conducive to: 1) forming operational definitions; 2) using mental models or theories; 3) developing investigatory skills; and 4) having the student learn through his own inquiries. The order of the textual content makes it possible to have a unified course with each new chapter providing a base for all that follows. The sequence of major topics in the text is:

Quantity of Matter: Mass
Characteristic Properties
Solubility and Solvents
The Separation of Substances
Compounds and Elements
Radioactivity
The Atomic Model of Matter
Size and Masses of Atoms and Molecules
Molecular Motion
Heat

There is an introduction to these topics and a short epilogue.

The laboratory experiments are a part of the textbook and constitute a substantial part of the course. If the IPS course is taught as it is intended, seventy-five per cent of the class time is spent in laboratory experiments and questions related to these investigations. Someone has described the IPS text-lab book as having more sentences ending with a question mark than a period. The organization of experiments uses previously developed skills in carrying out other experiments later. The first experiment in the course, distillation of wood, makes use of most of the major pieces of apparatus needed for the course and illustrates the experimental approach that will characterize its teaching. Much of the equipment is used throughout the year in various combinations and in this way laboratory skills are continually reinforced. The prelab and postlab discussions about an experiment clarify the goals of the experiment and encourage better interpretations of the observations. Some experiments are more quantitative in nature, requiring a careful recording and displaying of the data and a mathematical interpretation of its meaning. To improve the meaning of these experiments the data from an entire class is frequently pooled.

The IPS group recognized the need for simplified equipment useable in schools without specially designed laboratory rooms and with furniture consisting of no more than a flattop desk and a sink. The laboratory equipment for an experiment is assembled on a piece of pegboard which can be placed on any flat surface. Gas and electricity are *not* required for experiments. To carry out a student-centered laboratory program under these conditions required the development of new experiments and special apparatus. The cost for equipping a class of twenty-four students with all the equipment and supplies needed for a year is approximately $700, and for two sections of twenty-four students a total of $780 or two sections of thirty students $935. Around ten to twelve per cent of the lab materials are expendable during the year.

The laboratory notebook is a wire-bound book of quadrelle paper. Here the student directly records his notes and observations, and develops the write-up for each experiment. There are no directions in the notebook and the student is free to choose the most appropriate format for reporting his data.

The teacher's function in the IPS course is to maintain a climate of inquiry and to help guide the reasoning processes of students. He emphasizes ideas rather than facts; depends upon experimental results rather than assertion to develop concepts; encourages active discussion and thinking rather than passivity; and stimulates students to raise questions and to speculate from their observations. The teacher stresses precise communication and demonstrates ways in which this is achieved. Effective teaching of IPS requires a teacher who is clear in his understanding of the goals, has some feeling for the heuristics of science teaching, and appreciates the story line of the course.

Achievement tests covering two or three chapters in a series are available for the course. These tests have a reliability of around .80. Chapter quizzes are found in the Teacher's Guide. Five films are recommended for the course; four of these are from the PSSC series, and one, "Mass of Atoms," has been produced especially for IPS.

The *Teacher's Guide* is much larger than the student text and has: 1) directions for all experiments and demonstrations; 2) an overview of the major ideas for each chapter; 3) suggestions for teaching; 4) a teaching schedule; 5) a large selection of problems "for home, desk, and lab."; 6) suggestions for judging pupil achievement; and 7) answers to all problems and questions in the text. The guide is indispensable, especially the first two or three times one teaches the course.

Interaction of Matter and Energy (IME) is an experimentally developed physical science course specially designed for use at the ninth grade level. In 1959 a group of science teachers at Yuba City High School (California) outlined and taught a new course which they felt was more allied to a modern philosophy of science teaching than were the conventional textbooks. After several years of experimentation the authors, Norman Abraham, Patrick Balch, Donald Chaney and Lawrence M. Rohrbaugh, were satisfied they had a course plan ready for further research and evaluation. Three of the authors in the meantime had acquired considerable curriculum experience as participants and writers on BSCS courses. From this experience they recognized the value of extensively testing a new course before it is made available for other teachers to use. What is unique about this curriculum project is the sponsorship of a commercial publisher, Rand McNally and Company, for the field testing, teacher education and development of the course.

In 1965 a preliminary text was written and taught to 4,500 students by forty-five teachers during the 1965–66 school year. A revised form of the text, based upon feedback from the first year, was tested by 200 teachers and 19,000 students in 1966–67. In 1967–68 a third edition was used and evaluated by 300 teachers distributed throughout thirty-six states. By the spring of 1968 the course had been revised three times, based upon feedback from a total of 55,000 students and 550 teachers. Not only were these students asked to provide open-ended comments on the course, but the testing program at this stage of development was designed to ascertain the extent to which students were attaining the objectives and learning sought for concepts. The final edition of the text was published by Rand McNally and Company in 1968.

The rationale for the IME course is based upon an *inquiry* system of teaching and learning. Students are provided with opportunities to observe, investigate, interpret data, and formulate conclusions. They learn how to formulate a hypothesis, to use a scientific model, and to reason inductively. All of these processes are carried out in a context leading to the acquisition of basic scientific concepts.

The conceptual themes of IME are: 1) the nature of scientific behavior—experimental design, observation and interpretation; 2) the nature and use of scientific models; 3) the particulate and continuous nature of matter; 4) the conversion of energy from one form to another; 5) the continuous interaction of energy and matter; and 6) the behavior of matter and energy in living systems. The major topics of the course contributing to the themes are: 1) observing the behavior of matter; 2) models of atoms and molecules; 3) periodic classification of elements; 4) chemical and physical reactions; 5) phases of matter; 6) nature of heat and light; 7) time, speed, and distance relationship of objects in motion; 8) energy conversion and transfer; and 9) matter, energy, and processes of life. The course is divided into eighteen sections: 1) section one introduces the student to the characteristics of scientific activity; 2) sections two to six focus on chemical interactions; 3) sections seven to ten describe physical interactions; 4) sections eleven to fourteen deal with an intensive study of energy in non-living systems and the conversion of energy; 5) sections fifteen through eighteen treat the role of energy and the place of molecules in living systems. The content of the course makes it particularly suitable as a basis for BSCS biology. It can also serve as a physical science requirement for students who do not enroll in high school chemistry or physics.

The laboratory is central to the IME course and the seventy-one investigations included in the textbook provide the student with many opportunities for learning about the various facets of scientific inquiry. The student is continually involved in the course as an active learner. Experiments are designed so that students are unlikely to make satisfactory predictions of outcome unless they carry out the investigation. A separate laboratory manual is not required in the course. The textual materials provide a base for the laboratory activities, rather than providing answers.

The extensive laboratory program requires only a minimum of equipment which is of low cost. Most of it can be constructed by the teacher. If purchased the cost is approximately $400 for a class of twenty-five students, including teacher demonstration materials.

The mode of teaching required for the course demands students to explore and investigate through their own efforts. The text-lab book provides directions for student learning and the teacher assists where needed. One purpose for pretesting the course was to find activities highly motivating for young people that might serve to sustain independent learning.

The teacher's edition of the IME textbook provides information on subject matter, logistics, and teaching schedules for class and laboratory work. Suggestions are made for carrying out experiments and extending them; for selecting films and supplementary readings; and for teaching the course. Quarterly and final tests are available. These tests are designed to indicate student achievement of concepts and of inquiry.

BIOLOGY PROGRAMS

The *Biological Sciences Curriculum Study* (BSCS) began its activities in January, 1959 under the sponsorship of the American Institute of Biological Sciences (AIBS) and with the financial support of the National Science Foundation. Its activities have been guided by a steering committee of about thirty research biologists, high school biology teachers, science educators and school administrators. The study began with Bently Glass of The Johns Hopkins University as chairman of the Steering Committee. Arnold B. Grobman, of Florida State University, was named Director for the BSCS with John A. Moore, Columbia University, as Chairman of the Curriculum Committee, and Addison E. Lee, The University of Texas, as Chairman of the Laboratory Committee. In the first ten years of its operation over 2,000 biologists and specially competent persons have contributed to the development of its various programs. In general the efforts of the BSCS have been to: 1) produce modern biology courses (textbooks) for the spectrum of students who take biology in high school; 2) develop special resource materials for the teaching of these courses, such as, films, pamphlets, laboratory blocks, equipment, tests, and new experiments; 3) formualte programs and materials for both in-service and pre-service education of teachers so they may be better prepared to present the new biological course materials. Forty adaptations or translations of BSCS materials have been completed and others are under development. Some of the countries using BSCS courses are Australia, Brazil, Canada (French language), Columbia, China (Taiwan), India, Israel, Italy, Japan, Korea, New Zealand, the Philippines, Thailand, Turkey, Russia, ten countries in tropical America, fifteen English speaking countries in Africa, Denmark, Sweden, Mexico and others. The reform movement in biological education has become world-wide in scope. It should be recognized that new discoveries and developments in biological science over the past twenty years make a new school curriculum imperative if other than the history of biology is to be taught. From another point of view the problems of biology —behavior, population growth, genetics, disease, favorable life environments, food and others—are the problems of mankind, both personal and social.

The sciences related to a study of life forms are many and diverse. The debates about the nature of biology as a discipline and how its problems should be studied further represent the diversity among biologists. There are biologists who prefer to study the 'big picture,' the interrelationships among living things. Other biologists find it more interesting to seek explanations about plants and animals within their molecular structure. Since there is no one point of view about biology as a science it is not reasonable to think of the biology curriculum as being made up of a representative course. Thus the BSCS chose to prepare three courses in high school biology, each with a somewhat different emphasis and approach, but each representing a valid interpretation of the science of biology.

As a preliminary step to the development of a new curriculum a study was made of the research on biological education and of previous efforts to reform biology teaching from 1890 to 1960.[1] To help clarify the corrective measures they must undertake in developing new texts the BSCS Steering Committee informally examined commonly used pre-1960 biology textbooks. These were some of the reactions of the reviewers: 1) chapters or units were more or less discrete resulting in courses without conceptual unity; 2) much of the course content was outmoded or trivial in terms of modern biology; 3) little attention was devoted to the inquiry or investigative phases of biological science; 4) there was an overload of factual detail and names of things obscuring significant concepts; 5) important biological information, for example, organic evolution, human reproduction, growth and development, and racial characteristics, was either omitted, minimized, or erroneously presented; 6) topics were superficially treated without reference to related explanatory theories; 7) too much attention was devoted to the applications of biology in agriculture, health, and conservation without the benefit of developing the underlying biological principles; 8) the work of both the class and the laboratory was descriptive without

[1] Hurd, Paul DeHart. *Biological Education in American Secondary Schools 1890–1960*. BSCS Bulletin No. 1. Washington, D.C.: American Institute of Biological Sciences, 1961.

focus and the benefit of explanatory systems; 9) the laboratory work was mostly a series of exercises often giving a false impression of modern biological investigation; furthermore, it was almost entirely nonquantitative; 10) much of the course content was presented at the structure-function level and there was an undue emphasis on taxonomy; 11) pictures and drawings of plants and animals were not to scale nor was this indicated; 12) the content was not only at a low level of sophistication, but what was more serious it was presented as dogma. The nature of the tests and end-of-chapter questions for these texts were of the kind demanding a knowledge of isolated facts fostering rote memorization rather than understanding on the part of students.

The criteria used for defining the objectives of BSCS biology arose from seeking answers to the following questions: What is the significant knowledge of living things as they are known in modern biology: What is the structure of inquiry, processes and concepts, that best characterizes modern biology? What knowledge of living things, and what attitudes and skills relevant to modern biology, will contribute the most to students' personal lives and to the execution of their responsibilities as men and citizens? The answer to the first question evolved the unifying themes needed to bind together not only the various parts of each course but the several versions of BSCS biology. (These themes were identified in a previous chapter and are restated here for convenience and emphasis). The order and arrangement of the themes suggest their interconnections. Themes one to five identify the content of BSCS courses; themes eight and nine describe the logical structure of the courses; and themes six and seven concern both structure and content. These nine statements represent the major goals of the BSCS and identify the direction of teaching.

1. Change of living things through time: evolution
2. Diversity of type and unity of pattern in living things
3. The genetic continuity of life
4. The complementarity of organism and environment
5. The biological roots of behavior
6. The complementarity of structure and function
7. Regulation and homeostasis: preservation of life in the face of change
8. Science as inquiry
9. The history of biological conceptions.

These goals represent a balanced emphasis regarding modern biological thought and are not intended to provide an encyclopedic description of the biological sciences.

The specific objectives of BSCS biology, which initially guided the writing of the various courses, were in terms of the implications of the course for the student. The feeling was a study of biology should provide the student with:

1. An understanding of man's own place in the scheme of nature; namely, that he is a living organism and has much in common with all living organisms.
2. An understanding of his own body, its structure and function.
3. An understanding of the diversity of life and of the interrelations of all creatures.
4. An understanding of what man presently knows and believes regarding the basic biological problems of evolution, development, and inheritance.
5. An understanding of the biological basis of many of the problems and procedures in medicine, public health, agriculture and conservation.
6. An appreciation of the beauty, drama, and tragedy of the living world.
7. An understanding of the historical development of biology with examples of concepts to show how these are related to contemporary techniques, technology, and the nature of society.
8. An understanding of the nature of scientific inquiry: science is an open-ended intellectual activity and what is presently 'known' or believed is subject to 'change without notice'; the scientist in his work strives to be honest, exact—part of a community devoted to the pursuit of truth; his methods are increasingly exact and the procedures themselves are increasingly self-correcting.

Essentially these objectives define the teaching of biology in terms of its ongoing, self-corrective and revisionary inquiry processes and also as a body of currently warranted concepts and theories.

The basic curriculum program of BSCS consists of three distinct biology textbooks and related materials for use in the tenth grade of the American high school. Originally the three versions were classified in terms of their approach to biology:

1. classical (yellow)
2. ecological-evolutionary (green)
3. physiological-biochemical (blue)

Later, colors were assigned to each approach to identify the course and to recognize that none of the programs would fall clearly into one classification or another although the emphasis would be in a particular direction. When the courses were published commercially titles replaced the colors used to identify the experimental editions.

During the summer of 1960 the BSCS assembled three writing teams of high school biology teachers and university research biologists in about equal numbers to prepare preliminary trial materials in terms of the new goals and objectives. Trial centers were established in various sections of the country consisting of clusters of high schools located near to each other so the experimental teachers could meet frequently. In each center only one BSCS version was taught. During the 1960–61 school year BSCS materials were taught in 100 schools. Based on feedback the courses were rewritten during the summer of 1962 and the following school year taught in 500 schools; rewritten again in the summer of 1963 and taught in 950 schools the following year. By the time the textbooks and laboratory materials were ready for a commercial publisher they had been tested by over 1,000 teachers and 150,000 students in trial editions. With each writing of the texts, additional authorship was provided to insure maximum competence for preparing the materials. During the experimental years a total of twenty-five professional biological societies representing a larger number of disciplines reviewed the BSCS program and made recommendations. The experimental texts were published commercially in the spring of 1963. Each text version was published by a different company and by this procedure it was possible to maintain the separate identity of each book. During 1967, based upon feedback from thousands of teachers, the BSCS textbooks and related materials were again rewritten and second editions became available for school use with the fall semester 1968.

As the BSCS materials all have the same goals, conceptual themes, and objectives it is to be expected the versions are more alike than different. The BSCS texts are, however, quite different from traditional high school biology books. There is an estimated overlap of seventy per cent in topics included in the three BSCS versions, although the treatment of these topics is not identical. The remaining thirty per cent of each course represents the way a specific writing team views the structure of biology. From a curriculum point of view the three BSCS variations in content and organization have served to break the traditional pattern of biology courses, i.e., a phylogenetic approach overlain with life forms treated at the organ-tissue level of organization and from a structure-function concept of biology. The latter course design, sometimes called the "fern-frog" organization, was first laid out around 1860 to take advantage of Charles Darwin's newly proposed theory of evolution. In general the BSCS versions minimize organ-tissue concepts and concentrate more on the molecular and cellular at one extreme and the community, population and world biome at the other, with about the same attention to individual organisms as is found in conventional biology textbooks. The degree of emphasis upon these topic areas is different for each BSCS textbook. The Blue Version has its emphasis at the molecular level; the Green Version at the community; and the Yellow Version at the cellular.

The 1968 Blue Version, *Biological Science: Molecules to Man* published by Houghton Mifflin Company, has the following organization:

Unit One. Biology, the Interaction of Facts and Ideas: includes materials on science as inquiry, the variety of living things, conflicting views on the means of evolution, and the origin of living things.

Unit Two. Evolution of Life Processes: is a study of the forerunners of life, chemical energy for life, light as energy for life, and life with oxygen.

Unit Three. The Evolution of the Cell: presents master molecules, the biological code, and the cell theory.

Unit Four. Multicellular Organisms: New Individuals: considers the multicellular organism, reproduction, and development.

Unit Five. Multicellular Organisms: Genetic Continuity: includes patterns of heredity, genes and chromosomes, and the origin of new species.

Unit Six. Multicellular Organisms: Energy Utilization: is a study of transport, respiratory, digestive, and excretory systems.

Unit Seven. Multicellular Organisms: Unifying Systems: treats the regulatory, nervous, skeletal and muscular systems as well as the organism and behavior.

Unit Eight. Higher Levels of Organization: is a study of the human species, populations, societies and communities.

The laboratory investigations are included in the textbook and located at the place where they should be introduced. In addition, there are twenty supplementary investigations listed at the end of the textbook. The ten appendices to the book are on such topics as, units of measurement, the Krebs cycle, the chi-square test, and a catalog of nature, among others. There is a summary to each chapter highlighting the major ideas, plus a series of questions at three levels of sophistication, projects, and a bibliography.

BSCS Green Version, second edition 1968, *High School Biology,* published by Rand McNally and Company, is a combination textbook and laboratory manual. Field and laboratory investigations have been placed throughout the textbook as part of the learning resource on a particular topic. The content of the course represents an ecological approach to the study of biology and includes the following material:

Section One. The World of Life: the Biosphere: is a study of the web of life, individuals and populations, communities and ecosystems.

Section Two. Diversity Among Living Things: considers animals, plants and protists.

Section Three. Patterns in the Biosphere: examines patterns of life in the microscopic world, on land, in the water and in the past.

Section Four. Within the Individual Organism: explores the cell, bioenergetics, the functioning plant and animal, and behavior.

Section Five. Continuity of the Biosphere: is a study of reproduction, heredity and evolution.

Section Six. Man and the Biosphere: considers the human animal and man in the web of life.

Marginal notes throughout the text are there to assist the student in reading and understanding the text. At the end of chapters are lists of guide questions, problems, and suggested readings. The appendix includes a catalogue of living things and general suggestions for laboratory procedures.

Biological Science and Inquiry Into Life, second edition 1968, is the BSCS Yellow Version and it is published by Harcourt, Brace, and World, Inc. The content and sequence of topics in the book are:

Unit One. Unity: is a consideration of what biology is about, life from life, basic structure and functions, living chemistry, the physiology and reproduction of cells, and the hereditary materials.

Unit Two. Diversity: is a study of beginnings—viruses, bacteria, important small organisms, molds, yeasts and mushrooms, the trend toward complexity, the land turns green, photosynthesis, stems and roots— a study of complementarity of structure and function, reproduction and development in flowering plants, the world of animals, diversities among animals; digestion, transportation, respiration, excretion, homeostasis, coordination, support, locomotion, reproduction, and development in multicellular animals; and the analysis of behavior.

Unit Three. Continuity: includes patterns of heredity, the chromosome theory of heredity, Darwinian evolution, the mechanisms of evolution and the cultural evolution of man.

Unit Four. Interaction: is a study of animal balances in nature, ecosystems, and mankind: a population out of balance; and a perspective of time and life: molecules to man.

Student guide questions and problems are included in each chapter as well as related readings. Laboratory investigations are in a *Student Laboratory Guide,* a separate publication.

The major changes in the 1968 BSCS text versions compared with the 1963 books are those of updating the information to accommodate new developments in biology; a reordering of topics where experience has shown this to be needed; a rewriting of sections to simplify the reading and clarify meaning; a closer phasing of the laboratory into the textual materials. The underlying rationale of the BSCS program remains the same, that is, an emphasis upon pervasive biological concepts and upon the processes and means of scientific inquiry. It appears the 1968 BSCS versions have somewhat more topics in common than the 1963 versions, although the treatment of these topics remains unique with the version.

When a biology program is developed with new goals and subject matter, new tests of achievement need to be developed. The use of existing standardized tests reflecting different objectives and course content is not only improper but unfair to students. The BSCS has therefore, through its Test Construction Committee, developed a series of two comparable quarterly examinations for each of the three text versions. These tests were carefully designed for a high degree of BSCS validity, tested with students, revised, tested again, normed, and made available through the text publishers. Alternate Comprehensive Final Examinations for each text version may be purchased from the Psychological Corporation of New York. There are also specially written tests for the BSCS Second Course, *Biological Science: Interaction of Experiments and Ideas* and for the Special Materials, *Biological Science: Patterns and Processes.* A test is available to be used at the beginning of BSCS courses to gauge the student's grasp of the methods of scientific investigation, the *Processes of Science Test.* Three *Test Booklets,* one for each BSCS version, were prepared containing hundreds of questions which a teacher may select or modify to make his own tests. These booklets are available from the publishers of the basic texts. New test forms are obtainable for each of the 1968 BSCS courses. A Resource Book for Teachers, *Testing and Evaluating Student Success with Laboratory Blocks,* is available commercially to be used for assessing student achievement on the BSCS Blocks. Special attention has been given to the development of test instruments to measure inquiry objectives and process application throughout all of the BSCS tests.

There is a *Teacher's Guide* or *Manual* for each BSCS text version. They are written for use with a specific text version and while there are some variations, all contain supplementary information, answers to problems, suggestions for scheduling the course, useful teacher references on course content, suggested 16 mm. films for use with each chapter, as well as the use of the 8 mm. BSCS single topic inquiry films and pertinent information regarding laboratory equipment, and supplies. The *Teacher's Guides* are available from the version publishers.

A series of ten films on biological techniques used in BSCS courses has been produced primarily for viewing by teachers. The series includes bacteriological, histological, measuring, neurospora, smear and squash, weighing, and drasophila handling techniques. Other films in the series include culturing the slime mold plasmodium, paper chromotography and removing frog pituitary. These films are one to fourteen minutes long and are available in 16 mm. and Super-8, from Thorne Films, Boulder, Colorado.

The BSCS *Biology Teachers' Handbook,* published by John Wiley and Sons, New York, is intended to serve all the textbooks developed by the BSCS. The Handbook contains the resource materials for teaching science as "*enquiry*," these have been described in an earlier chapter of this book. Another part of the *Teacher's Handbook* explores the content, emphasis, themes, and objectives of BSCS biology. *Part III* offers a rigorous, minimal selection of material in physics, chemistry, and statistics relevant to the teaching of modern biology. Each chapter is written by an authority on the subject. In Parts *IV* and *V* are suggestions to facilitate the day-to-day teaching of biology. There are chapters on test construction and the conduct of discussions; bibliographies for both teacher and student; suggestions for the design of classrooms and laboratories and furniture requirements; a listing of sources of laboratory equipment and biological supplies; and a listing of teaching resources, such as, biological museums, arboretums, and zoological gardens. The *Handbook* provides information for the biology teacher interested in professional improvement and the teaching of modern biology, therefore it is not confined to any text version but serves all. A second edition of the *Handbook* is in preparation.

The BSCS through a wide variety of means has sought to assist pre- and in-service teachers to become acquainted with their goals and instructional materials. Consultant services have been made available to high schools and colleges when they have been requested. The BSCS staff has assisted in institute programs, participated in professional science teachers meetings, and published extensively in educational and scientific journals. There has been an active Teacher Preparation Committee since the inception of BSCS. Representative of the work of this committee is the publication *BSCS Materials for Preparation of In-Service Teachers of Biology* edited by Ted E. Andrews (Boulder: Biological Sciences Curriculum Study, 1964).

THE BSCS SPECIAL MATERIALS PROGRAM

The evaluation program for the three basic versions of BSCS biology revealed that between twenty to twenty-five per cent of the students in the tenth grade were below acceptable levels of achievement. A study of these students showed the majority: 1) scored below the fiftieth percentile on general aptitude tests; 2) read several years below grade level; 3) had difficulty with mathematical and verbal communication; and 4) had a poor academic record. In addition, they had a poor attitude toward school, they made few efforts to study, and were apathetic and indifferent. The underachiever, not a part of this study, was considered to be a different problem. The first effort to help the slow learner was the development of supplementary materials to accompany the regular text versions of BSCS. This did not prove to be effective and it was decided in 1963 to develop a biology textbook especially written for the academically unsuccessful student.

Several assumptions guided the work in preparing the new text, *Biological Science: Patterns and Processes;* these were: 1) the content should be the same biology offered other students but presented in a different way; 2) the goals of instruction should not deviate from the basic BSCS courses; and 3) the major changes should be reflected in the way the materials are organized, presented and taught. The last assumption means materials: 1) at a simpler reading level; 2) supported by multiple sensory aids; 3) developed to a large extent through laboratory work; 4) incorporating learning and study skills to develop good habits; and 5) adaptable to a wide range of student interests.

In the summer of 1963 a writing team for the 'slow learner' course was appointed consisting of high school biology teachers who had had experience teaching students for whom the new text was intended. Research biologists acted as consultants to verify the accuracy of the content and to suggest interesting laboratory possibilities. The first version of 'special materials' represented a pilot effort to ascertain the feasibility of the approach and to test some ideas about working with slow learners. This edition was used in thirty-seven schools during 1963–64. Based on teacher feedback and testing, the course was rewritten in the summer of 1964 and taught to 14,000 students by 300 teachers during the school year 1964–65. In 1966 the next text *Biological Science: Patterns and Processes* was published commercially by Holt, Rinehart and Winston, Inc.

The text is limited to a study of five major topics: 1) ecological relations; 2) cell energy processes; 3) reproduction and development; 4) genetic continuity; and 5) organic evolution. The book has a paper cover and the pages are both perforated for easy removal and punched to reassemble as a notebook. This makes it possible to distribute a few pages at a time and not overwhelm the student with a large volume of reading material. The laboratory activities and discussion problems are included in the text at points where they may best contribute to learning a topic. Where experience has shown the understanding of a topic is dependent upon very careful reading these topics are written in a programed form within the text itself. Drawings, pictures, and diagrams, liberally used, illustrate and reinforce topics. By limiting the course to only five major concepts of modern biology and by involving the student in many direct learning activities the writers believe the topics can be taught to the same level of comprehension acquired by students of higher academic ability. There are not as many biological ideas in the slow learner course as in the basic BSCS courses, but the commitment is to understanding, not a superficial covering of many topics.

The *Teacher's Handbook* for the special materials course is a detailed though flexible guide. It paces each of the five divisions of the textbook by identifying the major *ideas* the student is expected to acquire while studying this section of the course. For example, in the section on reproduction and development, the student is expected to acquire an understanding of the following ideas: 1) life comes from life; 2) by the process of reproduction, living things insure the continuity of their own kind; 3) asexual reproduction is one method by which the continuity of life is insured and the offspring produced normally resemble the parent closely; 4) sexual reproduction is another means of insuring the continuity of life and involves specialized cells called gametes; 5) the union of the gametes—fertilization—begins the development of a new individual; 6) there is a definite observable pattern of growth after fertilization; 7) patterns of sexual reproduction are similar in plants and animals; 8) similar patterns of development may be observed in other multi-cellular organisms; 9) similar favorable environmental conditions are necessary for the maintenance of embryonic development; 10) mammals, including man, have also developed successful reproductive mechanisms; 11) one aspect of growth is the increase in number of cells which is accomplished by a process called mitosis; 12) cells differentiate during the growth of an organism. In the total course there are sixty-two of these "ideas." There is a wide range of instructional materials available to help make these ideas meaningful for the student. These materials also make it possible for the teacher to diversify his efforts. From class to class the pattern of teaching resources used might be quite different although the student's conceptual outcome is the same. At the end of the school year, after nine months of instruction, a student in intellectual possession of the sixty-two ideas of this course could no longer be considered an unsuccessful learner.

The entire cogency of the BSCS slow learner course rests upon having appropriate teaching materials and compatible instructional methods that capitalize on the *strengths* of the unsuccessful learner. This is the first of the national experimental science courses designed to be effective with this particular segment of the school population. This program is also the first to be preceded by a thorough study of what needed to be done in pedagogical terms and in the design of a textbook to make it reasonably acceptable to students. The revised edition of the text will be based upon student and teacher feedback from the first edition and will be available for use in 1970.

The BSCS Gifted Student Program

The science curriculum reform movement in its early phases was directed toward providing increased learning opportunities and challenges for the gifted and the talented student. Cole's Book on *Encouraging Scientific Talent* did much to define the problem with regard both to science teaching and the needs of society.[2] One of the early special committees appointed by the BSCS had as its function the study of the gifted high school student as a person, his performance in the classroom, and the special opportunities for his development provided by schools. The final report of this committee was published as BSCS Bulletin No. 2.[3] In essence the committee felt that gifted student science aptitudes would develop most through opportunities to engage in biological research.

It was apparent to the Gifted Student Committee that research problems challenging to gifted students must have special characteristics, such as: 1) the problem must not have a known answer; 2) the problem must be small enough to be reasonable to a high school student, but this should not mean a solution is assured; 3) the experimental problem should be practical in terms of cost and equipment needs; and 4) the student should be under "the gentle burden of independent research" and learning to cope with a problem. To obtain investigations with these characteristics the committee wrote to thousands of biologists asking them to prepare a prospectus for a piece of research, preferably in their field of interest. The replies were examined by a committee of high school biology teachers with long experience in teaching gifted students. Experiments that were not feasible for a high school student or too demanding of equipment were eliminated from consideration. Beginning in 1963 four volumes of these research studies, a total of 160 problems, have been published under the general title *Research Problems in Biology*. The

[2] Cole, Charles C. Jr. *Encouraging Scientific Talent*. New York: College Entrance Examination Board, 1956.

[3] Brandwein, P. F., Metzner, J., Morholt, E., Roe, A., and Rosen, W. *Teaching High School Biology: A Guide to Working With Potential Biologists*. Washington, D.C.: American Institute of Biological Sciences, 1962.

publisher is Anchor Books, Doubleday and Company, Garden City, New York.

The investigations cover a wide area of biological fields including animal behavior, animal and plant physiology, ecology, genetics, microbiology, and growth and development. Representative problems are: 1) control of growth of certain plant viruses by proteins; 2) the effect of chemicals on the regeneration of hydra; 3) the variation in electrical resistance of the human skin with physical activity; 4) sex differentiation in higher plants; and 5) secondary succession. Each investigation is introduced with the name and address of the biologist who suggested the problem. This means the student knows of at least one other person interested in the topic who may offer some helpful suggestions if requested. There is a short background discussion on the problem with suggestions or a hypothesis for a possible approach to the research. Comments regarding techniques, equipment, materials, and cautions are made for each study. General references for background reading and specific references to related research are listed. Since the problems are all unsolved there is no danger of 'giving away' the answer. If the student carries through the investigation in a satisfactory manner he potentially has a publishable paper for a biological journal. The rationale underlying this program is that gifted and creative students should be challenged at their own ability level and with materials that allow them to experience the satisfaction of an original endeavor.

The BSCS Second Level Course

About ten per cent of the high schools offer a second or advanced biology course. It is estimated that about 175,000 students take these courses. The curriculum reform movement has served to increase the number of advanced science courses in schools. The nature of these courses is so diverse as to make it virtually impossible to outline a typical program. Frequently they are listed for gifted students and those planning careers in biologically related fields. The prerequisite is usually an elementary biology course completed with a grade of "B+" or "A." The subject matter of the advanced course is more often than not a college level general biology textbook or a program designated as *Advanced Placement Biology*. Recently more schools allow the student to work on research projects; these are more or less independent of a prescribed course. Less common are specialized courses, such as, vertebrate anatomy and physiology, bacteriology, botany, zoology, ecology, and horticulture. These courses are taught from introductory college textbooks with a strong emphasis on laboratory work. At other times the advanced course is the training program for laboratory assistants to help teachers in beginning biology. There are many other variations, but for the most part goals are not clearly defined and the courses are short-lived. They are sustained by the special interest and enthusiasm of one teacher and all too frequently represent an overload in his teaching schedule.

In 1961 the BSCS began a three-year study of second level biology both to define more clearly its purposes and to prepare a course compatible with these goals. It was assumed the course should be specially written for the high school student and not be an adaptation of a college level text serving objectives peculiar to college programs.

The rationale underlying the second level course was: 1) it should build upon the concepts of biology taught in the first level course, complementing rather than repeating topics; 2) it should make use of the learning in cognate courses, such as, chemistry, physics and mathematics; 3) it should approach the teaching of biology from a laboratory or investigatory point of view; and 4) each topic should be taught in an inquiry and conceptual context and within the structure of a sequence of ideas. To accomplish these objectives the Committee found it desirable to base the initial course on a series of BSCS laboratory blocks with supplementary materials to provide coherence. BSCS "invitations to enquiry" were used to develop concepts related to the processes of science. In addition students were expected: 1) to make a statistical analysis of observations from the laboratory so data might be better evaluated; 2) to know how to read scientific literature; 3) to understand the meaning of modern controversy in biology and its relation to the generation of new knowledge; and 4) to appreciate the impact of science upon modern society. A preliminary text written with these goals in mind was tested during the 1962–63 school year by twenty-two teachers and their 650 students. The feedback showed the sequencing of BSCS lab blocks with connecting materials was undesirable, but the goals established for the course were acceptable. The course was redesigned in the summer of 1963 and tested in seventy schools with 2,200 students during the 1963–64 school year. The revised experimental text was again rewritten, using information from the 1963–64 test centers. A final version, titled *Biological Science: Interaction of*

Experiments and Ideas, was published commercially by Prentice-Hall Inc. in 1965.

The content of the new course consists of:

Part one—The Nature of Biological Science
Phase one—An orientation to the meaning of science and the role of inquiry in biology.
Phase two—Processes of biological investigation, such as, principles of experimental design, uncertainty in science, probability and tests of significant differences, and searching the literature.

Part two—Experiments and Ideas in Biological Investigations
Phase three—Growth and interactions of populations including population dynamics, methods of studying populations, mutation frequency, and interactions with and following cell contact.
Phase four—Growth, development, and behavior of individuals, with topics on the life history of a flowering plant, growth and development in animals, regeneration, hormonal regulation and animal behavior.

Part three—Conclusions and Beginnings
Phase five—Science and society with discussions on the responsibilities of the scientist and the role of controversy in science.

A series of thirty-eight investigations provides the vehicle for developing the concepts in parts one and two of the text. Part three is a series of essays by outstanding scientists.

The Teacher's Edition of *Biological Science: Interaction of Experiments and Ideas* contains all the pages in reduced form of the student text plus a commentary on each investigation, and appendices on laboratory requirements, preparation of chemical solutions and media, maintenance of living organisms, mathematics tables, and an extensive bibliography for each section of the book. A new edition of the BSCS second level text and teacher's edition was published in 1969.

The BSCS Laboratory Blocks

One of the BSCS curriculum innovations has been the development of *Laboratory Blocks* to introduce students to the characteristics of biological research. The Blocks, built around a single biological topic, are written to involve the student in a six weeks' long laboratory venture. During this time most of what he learns about a topic is the result of his own observations and experimentally collected data. A Block is a carefully planned continuous series of laboratory experiences in 'structured discovery' by means of which the student, though guided, learns independently of a textbook. He is involved in a way of learning that characterizes all of science—observation and experimentation. From direct participation in a research endeavor he is more likely to develop an appreciation of the spirit of science and an understanding of scientific inquiry than from teaching methods based upon assertion and with subject matter that is little more than thinly disguised dogma.

Each Block has been written by one or more research biologists whose particular interest is the subject dealt with in the Block. The pattern for writing, classroom testing, revising, and equipment development was the responsibility of the BSCS Committee on Innovation in Laboratory Instruction. The Blocks may be used with any of the BSCS textbooks, sequenced to form an independent course, or in combination with other biology textbooks or courses of study. When used with a BSCS textbook the subject matter of the Block replaces the corresponding section in the text. A guide to the course adjustments needed for each Block is found in the BSCS Special Publication No. 5.[4] The thirteen Blocks in the series are:

Animal Growth and Development
Complementarity of Structure and Function
Plant Growth and Development
Microbes: Their Growth, Nutrition and Interaction
Field Ecology
Regulation in Plants by Hormones
Life in the Soil
Animal Behavior
Genetic Continuity
The Molecular Basis of Metabolism
Physiological Adaptation
The Biological Effects of Radiation
Evolution

Each of the Blocks is a separate publication with both a Student's Edition and a Teacher's Supplement, published by D. C. Heath and Co.

Two correlated books have been written to supplement the use of the Blocks: *Innovations in Equipment and Techniques for the Biology Teaching Laboratory,* and a resource book for teachers,

[4] Lee, A., Lehman, D. L., Peterson, G. F. (Editors). *Laboratory Blocks in Teaching Biology*. Special Publication No. 5. Boulder: BSCS, 1967.

Testing and Evaluating Student Success with Laboratory Blocks. D. C. Heath and Co. is the publisher for both volumes.

The Laboratory Committee of BSCS is developing a series of experiments entitled "Take Home Laboratories." These laboratories all have the following characteristics: 1) they are of short duration; 2) they deal with a single aspect of an experimental situation; 3) they require little if any equipment or supplies beyond that normally available outside a classroom; 4) they are designed to test a single hypothesis, but may be extended; 5) the directions are not of the detailed cookbook kind, but rather more generalized outlines of an approach to a problem; and 6) they are designed for the student to do outside of class as an extra assignment or on his own initiative. The Committee is also writing Laboratory Blocks of two to three weeks in length, laboratory programs built around the extensive study of a single organism, and programs for independent study. All of these programs reflect the notion that an important outcome from the study of any science is the inquiry procedures which make concepts knowable and useable.

BSCS Single Topic Inquiry Films

An important supplement to the BSCS basic texts is the single topic Super 8 loop film designed specially to aid teachers in presenting biology as inquiry and as a way of thinking. Nearly five years were spent investigating techniques and the means by which this could be accomplished through the media of films. The requirement was one of finding a way to actively involve a student with the film in contrast to his usual role as a passive observer. Instructional films usually 'tell a story' or explain something visually; it was exactly this the BSCS wished to avoid, and to find an approach more conducive to inquiry and concept attainment. A number of pilot films were produced, tested with students, and modified until a valid format was developed.

The present BSCS Single Topic Films require four to five minutes of viewing time. Typically they present experimental data, or visual phenomena (mitosis, for example), or an environmental scene (requiring an interpretation such as, mountain trees) or a biological problem (the importance of the nucleus). Although the basic approach in the films is the same, each differs in level of difficulty, and in emphasis on the various elements of scientific inquiry. Some stress the role of critical observation; others require the interpretation of observations and data, the identification of a problem, the formulation of hypotheses, or the design of an experiment. With the viewing of each film the student not only learns something about inquiry but extends his knowledge of biology.

There is a separate teacher's guide for each film outlining the general method for its presentation, providing background information for the teacher, and describing student responses and teacher activities required for the most effective use of the film. The films are designed to be stopped at specified frames in order to raise questions, to provide an opportunity for a longer period of observation, to record data, to hold a class discussion, or to decide from observations to this point what is likely to follow. It is necessary, therefore, for the projector to have a 'stop-frame' device.

The first series of twenty BSCS single topic inquiry films includes some of the following titles: 1) Social Behavior in Chickens; 2) Convergence; 3) Water and Desert Plants; 4) An Inquiry—The Importance of the Nucleus; 5) Mimicry; 6) Temperature and Activity in Reptiles. The films are available from the publishers of BSCS textbooks. While the BSCS films reflect BSCS goals, they may be used with any biology course to teach inquiry.

BSCS Biology Reading Series

The first special project of the BSCS was the development of a series of pamphlets each on a single biological topic. The series was planned to provide a highly interesting and an authoritative treatment of a topic in language understandable to the layman. The pamphlets were to be no more than thirty-six pages with many illustrations. Several purposes were to be served by these publications: 1) students interested in a special topic would have a short, up-to-date reference; 2) teachers would have a ready means for either informing themselves or keeping up-to-date on a wide range of biological topics; 3) laymen interested in biology would have a report they could be expected to understand, since the pamphlet series is based upon the assumptions the reader will not have more background than that provided by a high school biology course.

The plan was to release the pamphlets on a monthly basis, eight publications per year. The first series was published during the school year 1962–63 and was followed by two more series for a total of twenty-four issues. Bound volumes of the first three series of pamphlets are available from D. C. Heath and Co. After an interval of several years a new series was started in 1966 under the general title *Patterns of Life Series,* published by Rand McNally and Company. The concept of the BSCS pamphlets remains the same but the format is changed and the publication averages close to sixty pages.

Illustrative titles in the Heath series are: 1) Guides to Animal Navigation; 2) Biological Clocks; 3) Population Genetics; 4) Homeostatic Regulation; 5) Animal Language; 6) Hibernation. The Rand McNally series includes: 1) Population Dynamics; 2) Dynamic Equilibrium; 3) Singing Insects; 4) Ecology of Intertidal Zones; 5) The Impact of Fungi on Man; 6) Antibiotics.

A third series of forty paperback books is under development by BSCS intended primarily for the layman. These will be on interesting and controversial biological topics and issues facing every individual in our society today. Some of these subjects are birth control, air and water pollution, mental health, human genetics and congenital defects, cell biology and cancer, and psychotherapy and human behavior. Pegasus Press is the series publisher.

BSCS BIOLOGY IMPLEMENTATION IN THE SCHOOLS

The introduction of a new science curriculum into a school has implications for laboratory facilities and equipment, and school organization. As we have seen, the BSCS program is heavily laboratory oriented with experiments new to high school biology. Equipment and supplies are needed to support the investigative phase of the textbook, each of the thirteen laboratory blocks requires some special materials, and the Research Problems in Biology have other demands. Typical of all of the new science courses developed during the reform movement, the costs for equipment and supplies for the 'new' courses is less than for the 'old' if the school is being stocked for the first time. A school already equipped, having the average range of supplies and equipment, will need to make additional expenditures to support the new program. However, it is not necessary to provide materials beyond those needed for one text version and one laboratory block to begin. If the special materials, basic, and second level courses are all taught in the same school additional supplies will be required.

The BSCS has published extensive lists of equipment and supply needs for all their programs. Class and laboratory arrangements and management have also been studied and good practices identified. The sources for this information are:

1. Grobman, Hurd, Klinge, Lawler and Palmer. *BSCS Biology—Implementation in the Schools.* Boulder: Biological Sciences Curriculum Studies, 1964.
2. Barthelemy, Dawson, Lee. *Innovations in Equipment and Techniques for the Biology Teaching Laboratory.* Boston: D. C. Heath and Co., 1963.
3. BSCS Teacher Preparation Committee. *Laboratory Blocks in Teaching Biology.* Boulder: Biological Sciences Curriculum Study, 1967. See also the *Teacher's Supplement* for each BSCS Laboratory Block, available from D. C. Heath and Co.
4. The *Teacher's Guide* for each text version contains a list of equipment and supply needs.
5. See also issues of the *BSCS Newsletter,* particularly numbers 9, 15, 21, 25, and 29.
6. Biological supply houses have developed unofficial but quite accurate lists of BSCS laboratory requirements.

It has not been the policy of the science curriculum reform groups to develop programs demanding radical changes in school organization or requiring a substantial outlay of money in order to adopt a new program. In fact they have been criticized for adjusting the new programs to traditional school schedules, organizations, and facilities and neglecting their resources for developing new ventures into these areas.

CHEMISTRY PROGRAMS

I. Chemistry—An Experimental Science

The discontent about the teaching of chemistry in high school resembles the other sciences: the course content was often out-of-date and sometimes incorrect; little use was made of theory; a descriptive and static picture of chemical systems was presented rather than structural and dynamic processes; memorization of factual information received more attention than the acquisition of concepts and the development of understanding. Particularly depressive were the usual chemistry experiments verifying the known, the recording of uninterpreted observations, and the endless balancing of equations without understanding the relationships or the mechanisms underlying the reactions.

A committee established in 1959 by the American Chemical Society under the chairmanship of A. B. Garrett of Ohio State University outlined the basic ideas for a Chemical Education Material Study (CHEM Study). The committee, composed of college and high school chemistry teachers recommended a reorganization of the conventional high school chemistry course. Glen T. Seaborg, a Nobel laureate in chemistry, was asked to be chairman of the revision program, and J. A. Campbell of Harvey Mudd College, Claremont, California, was named director. A steering committee for the project was named consisting of high school teachers, educators, and representatives from industry and government.

The educational rationale and approach to chemistry recommended by CHEM Study was to the effect important concepts and generalizations of chemistry should be developed inductively, based on data the student can understand, and wherever possible gathered directly by him in the laboratory. When this is impractical, data are obtained from teacher demonstrations, films, or from experiments described in the textbook. Class discussions and the textual treatment of a concept proceed on the basis students have observed the essential requirements in the laboratory. The laboratory is seen as a place to develop new ideas and to raise questions. In this way students will acquire some understanding of the nature of scientific investigation, the uncertainties and limitations inherent in all scientific work, and feel the excitement coming from discovering something for themselves. This is why the CHEM Study course stresses the experimental nature of chemistry. In CHEM Study explicit laboratory instructions for making observations are given but the experiment is 'open-ended' as to results and interpretations. The laboratory is a place where the student seeks regularities in what he observes and then 'wonders why.'

Chemistry, from the chemist's point of view, is not a study of reagents and their products but of the mechanisms by which reagents are changed to products. Thus the emphasis in the course is on structural chemistry and chemical dynamics. The focus of CHEM Study can be illustrated as follows:

(Not here) *Chemistry* (Not here)
REAGENTS ⟶ PRODUCTS
is here

Descriptive chemistry and industrial processes are used as examples of how concepts of chemistry are applied and to show the relationships between chemical concepts and theories, and technological developments.

The major educational goals of the CHEM Study program are:

1. To diminish the separation between scientists and teachers in the understanding of science.
2. To stimulate and to prepare those high school students whose purpose it is to continue the study of science in college as a profession.
3. To encourage teachers to improve their teaching methods by studying chemistry courses which are geared to keep pace with advanced scientific frontiers.
4. To further, in those students who will not continue the study of chemistry courses after high school, an understanding of the importance of science in current and future human activities.

The specific teaching objectives are related to presenting chemistry as a science representative of human activities. One purpose for teaching chemistry is to give the student a sense of the significance of these activities. The course objectives focus upon the student understanding: where do facts come from and what does it mean to "explain facts?" More specifically the student is expected:

1. To accumulate information through experimental observations.
2. To organize information and to observe regularities; to evaluate and to interpret data.
3. To use a model system to account for observed behavior.
4. To communicate experimental findings to others.
5. To appreciate the meaning of uncertainty in science and why certainty is not possible.
6. To recognize a theory or law need not be correct in every context to be useful.
7. To recognize there is no assurance a law established within a certain range of experience applies outside of this experience.
8. To understand the implications of a law (prediction) lead to experiments outside the range of experience upon which the law is based. Interpolation and extrapolation are forms of prediction.
9. To appreciate laws in agreement with presently recognized data may, nevertheless, be changed or abandoned in the future as additional experiments increase our knowledge. Science is not a completed structure but a growing one.

10. To be able to use the simplest cycle of scientific activity—observe; find regularity; find explanations (hidden regularities).
11. To recognize science could not advance if our overwhelming mass of knowledge were not ordered with the aid of theories and laws.
12. To appreciate all scientific knowledge is derived from experimental observations.

It is hoped a student will leave the course knowing chemistry in terms of the structure of a system and its dynamics. This means not only electron structure, but also the geometrical arrangement of atoms, relative sizes and shapes of atoms, the packing of atoms and molecules, the forces between them, and how these conditions influence chemistry.

The writing of the CHEM course began in June, 1960 at Harvey Mudd College. Nine college chemists and nine high school chemistry teachers developed the first trial edition of the textbook and laboratory materials. The writing team used the following criteria to select the subject matter for the course:

1. Is the idea so important that no first course is complete without it?
2. Can the idea be developed honestly at a level comprehensible to high school students?
3. Can it be developed out of experimental evidence high school students can gather or, at least, understand?
4. Does it tie into other parts of the course so its use will be reinforced by practice?

Materials meeting these four criteria are organized to present chemistry as a consistent flowing aspect of man's insight into the natural world rather than as a discrete series of isolated facts. Introductory chapters present an overview of chemistry in terms of the atomic-molecular nature of substances and stress concepts of chemical behavior using the atomic theory and energy changes. The periodic table is introduced as a means of ordering chemical information. The objective is to provide a framework into which additional information can be fitted later. The second section of the text explores some of the most basic concepts of chemistry. Such topics as energy and rates of chemical change, equilibrium, acid-base, and oxidation-reduction are tied together in terms of the mole concept, the kinetic theory, and the atomic-molecular concept of matter. The work of the second semester begins with the concept of atomic and molecular structure, followed by the structural relationships in the phases of matter, and their influence on chemical activity. The final section of the course describes the chemistry of carbon and of typical elements in the periodic table as one moves through the rows and columns of the table. In these chapters, concepts and theories taught earlier in the course are again brought forth to help crystalize the idea of the structure of chemistry.

Once the course was written it was tested in twenty-four high schools the first year, 1960–61; it was then revised, rewritten, and taught to 12,000 students in 1961–62. Utilizing feedback and the experience of the experimental teachers from the first two trial years the course materials were further reorganized, rewritten, expanded, and this time taught to 45,000 students in 560 high schools. This number of students was equal to a four per cent sample of all taking chemistry that year. The final version of the CHEM Study materials was published in 1963 by the W. H. Freeman Company of San Francisco and includes a textbook, laboratory manual, and teacher's guide.

There is a teaching style upon which CHEM Study depends if the course objectives are to be achieved. It may be broadly described as maintaining within the classroom an inquiring atmosphere. More specifically, the concepts and ideas about chemistry are developed inductively. Experiments are carried out *before* the associated readings are assigned in the textbook and before the topic is discussed in class. While there is a prelab discussion before each experiment it is done so as not to reveal its outcome. The laboratory experiments are designed to encourage students to think about their efforts through seeking regularities in their observations, and attempting to explain why they exist. While the experiments have a specified procedure they are open-ended in terms of results and interpretations. The inquiry environment is maintained through the students' conversations among themselves in the laboratory and the teacher-student postlab discussions. Furthermore, the laboratory 'write-ups' are not prescribed as to style or method; the student chooses the means he feels are most effective for communicating the results of his investigation. The CHEM Study authors envisioned the course as not one in which the student listens while the teacher talks about science, but one in which there is a minimum of lecturing and a substantial amount of class discussion based upon direct observation and reading. These discussions often lead to further experimentation growing out of experiments done previously.

Similarly to many of the other nation-wide experimental science courses, supporting instructional materials were developed to assure the best use of the program. At the completion of the first phase of CHEM Study the following materials had been produced:

Text—*Chemistry: An Experimental Science;* W. H. Freeman and Company; San Francisco: 1963.
Laboratory Manual—*Chemistry: An Experimental Science Laboratory Manual;* W. H. Freeman and Company; San Francisco: 1963.
Teacher's Guide—*Chemistry: An Experimental Science Teacher's Guide;* W. H. Freeman and Company; San Francisco: 1963.
Tests—CHEM Study, open-book achievement tests; series 1962–63; series 1963–64; series 1964–65; W. H. Freeman and Company, 660 Market Street, San Francisco, California, 94104.
Films—*Teacher's Guide to the CHEM Study Chemistry Films;* Modern Learning Aids, 3 East 54th Street, New York, New York 10022; 1964.
Programed Sequences—*Slide Rule,* and *Exponential Notation;* W. H. Freeman and Company: San Francisco, 1963.

The *text* has twenty-five chapters although the authors intended the 'normal' chemistry class to complete only the first seventeen and one or two in the last section of the book. The text contains frequent references to laboratory activities as a constant reminder chemistry is an experimental science.

The *laboratory manual* is separate from the textbook but integrated with it. The instructions include many questions to cue student thinking, but unless the experiment is performed and thought about, it is not likely to be understood.

The *Teacher's Guide* is organized into chapters corresponding with those of the student's textbook. Each chapter of the guide contains the following information:

1. Intent and approach to the textbook, a section discussing the overall philosophy.
2. A brief outline of the text chapter.
3. A list of the major new concepts.
4. A suggested time schedule and notes on lab preparations for future experiments.
5. A section-by-section discussion of the textbook and notes on each laboratory experiment.
6. A listing of supplementary teaching materials including films, monographs, articles and books for student reading and teacher reference.

7. A background discussion of the chemical principles and scientific philosophy for the teacher's benefit.
8. Answers and a discussion on each exercise and problem in the course.
9. A list of open-book quiz questions and answers—more than enough for each chapter.

The *laboratory notebook* is for the student to keep as a permanent record of his observations, calculations, interpretations and questions. The notebook is arranged to allow a carbon copy of what is written; the original copy is handed in each day and the carbon is retained for study, reference and further notes at the time of the postlab discussion.

The *teacher's guide to individual experiments* contains the rationale for each experiment; a briefing on the prelab discussion; equipment needed; time required for an experiment based upon a fifty-minute class period; precautions; laboratory hints; outline for the postlab discussion; answers to questions; suggestions for reporting the experiment; a list of questions for the student to wonder about; extensions of the experiment—extracurricular investigations; use of laboratory and class facilities; film resources; and a complete list of chemical and equipment needs.

There are three sets of CHEM tests—Series 1962–63; Series 1963–64; and Series 1964–65. Each set includes unit tests, semester, and final examinations. All the tests are of a multiple choice type and intended for open-book use. The questions emphasize the understanding of principles and their application to new situations.

Each *CHEM Study* film is designed to be used with a specific topic in the course. Although the course can be taught without the film, to do so lessens the effectiveness of the teaching. The films were designed with two main purposes in mind: 1) to bring into the classroom important experimental evidence which is difficult or impractical to introduce through student experiments or teacher demonstrations; and 2) to clarify, through animation, the mental models of structure and of dynamic processes which help scientists and students make sense out of the experimental evidence. Twenty-six films with Teacher's Guides are available for purchase or rental. There are also two 16 mm. in-service teacher education films; one of these is suitable for administrators and parents. *CHEM Study: Information For Educators* is a film providing information on costs and the logistics involved in introducing CHEM Study into a school system. *A Chance To Wonder Why* is a film showing a typical CHEM Study class in action; it is suitable for parents as well as teachers. There is a *Teachers Guide* for each film containing a statement of its purpose, suggested pre-showing and post-showing class activities, a detailed outline of the film's content, and supplementary material which may help the teacher.

The CHEM Study program requires no special *facilities* beyond those of the typical high school chemistry laboratory. The special equipment and chemicals needed for the CHEM course may cost as much as $300 the first year.

The CHEM Study course is now available in *four* versions, the original (1963) and three revised editions (1968) of the original textbook. Each textbook is published by a different book company and has its separate author team. By 1965 it became apparent that the original CHEM Study textbook needed revision to correct some errors, to improve its readability, to up-date its content, and to modify its organization. At the time the Steering Committee made its decision to revise the course the original version had been taught to over 300,000 students. Suggestions for refining the course had been collected over a period of several years from both teachers and students. Experience with the CHEM course had demonstrated its curriculum and pedagogical advantages as well as its educational rationale. The Steering Committee, recognizing it had developed one effective model for the teaching of high school chemistry, felt it could serve as a model for other chemistry courses with a different authorship. In October of 1965 the CHEM Study Steering Committee invited publishers to submit proposals for a revision of the CHEM Study program. It was agreed in advance that no less than three different interpretations of the original courses would be considered by the Steering Committee. The criteria used to select publishers for the revisions were: 1) the author team must have had experience with CHEM Study; 2) the proposed revision must be compatible with the CHEM Study philosophy and teaching approach; and 3) the company must have experience in publishing high school textbooks. The three publishers selected from the seven bidding for the revision opportunity were Houghton Mifflin, Prentice-Hall, and Raytheon.

Chemistry: An Investigative Approach, the CHEM Study revision developed by Houghton Mifflin and Co. (1968) carefully follows the CHEM Study philosophy. Some of the revision features are:

1) there are unit and chapter introductions; 2) capsule summaries follow each section of the text; 3) exercises have been renamed "self check" and are grouped at the end of sections rather than being dispersed within the sections; 4) there is a glossary of key chemical terms; 5) a laboratory supplement of ten experiments has been added; 6) laboratory experiments are a part of the textbook proper; 7) photographs of high school students have been added to demonstrate correct laboratory procedures; 8) fifteen original CHEM Study lab experiments have been dropped; 9) the original sequence of chapters has been rearranged to the following sequence: 1, 2, 4, 5, 6, *14, 15, 16, 17, 13,* 7, 8, 9, 10, 11, 12, *19, 21, 20,* 22, 23, *18,* 24, and 25; and 10) chapters 11 and 17 have been rewritten and chapters 18 and 25 rearranged. At one point there are 141 pages of text material without a contributing laboratory experiment. More attention is given to scientists such as Boyle and Charles, the practical uses of chemistry are stressed, and pictures of industrial manufacturing plants are prominent.

Chemistry: Experiments and Principles is the CHEM Study revision by the Raytheon Education Company. It also follows closely the rationale of the original course. There has been some reorganization of the sequence; for example, the chapters on bonding in CHEM Study (14, 15, 16, 17) are now chapters 8, 9, and 10 in the Raytheon edition. The text and laboratory manual are combined, but there are changes in emphasis. The present text has twenty experiments in the first eight chapters, whereas the original CHEM Study text had only twenty-three experiments by chapter fourteen. The Raytheon authors have given careful consideration to the use of analogies and to stress material familiar to the student, and seek to build upon topics taught earlier in the course. An effort has been made to keep the reading difficulty of the textbook at the eleventh grade level. Each chapter has an introduction, relating the content of the chapter to experiments or text material previously covered, as well as a chapter review. Thirty-five teacher demonstrations have been added to the course. Biographic sketches of prominent scientists have been deleted. The *Teachers Guide* is in two parts, one for the textbook and one for the laboratory; this permits the laboratory part (minus suggested quiz questions and problem answers) to be kept in the stockroom. There are forty-six experiments in the course, the same number found in the original text, but eleven of the CHEM Study experiments have been dropped and eleven new experiments added.

The Prentice-Hall version of CHEM Study, *Chemistry: Experimental Foundations* (1969), will follow the original philosophy and themes of the course. The new authors, all members of the original CHEM Study writing team, hope to make the revision more teachable. The content has been rearranged slightly to obtain a more logical sequence in the course. All definitions have been made operational in the sense new concepts are developed in a natural and logical way from a series of operations performed in the laboratory. An attempt has been made to keep analogies within the everyday experience of students. Historical materials have been introduced at the point of relevance to reinforce particular topics. The original CHEM Study policy regarding the use of technological and industrial applications has been sustained—they are not used. New experiments have been added to the course and others rewritten to make them more workable. All drawings of apparatus have been replaced with photographs. End-of-chapter summaries are more concise and partially replaced with a pre-chapter 'focus' to guide the student through what otherwise might seem to him a veritable maze of new ideas and concepts. New demonstrations have been developed to more clearly illustrate certain concepts. The format of the new textbook, laboratory manual, and teacher's guide are the result of feedback from teachers using the original version. The *Laboratory Manual* is being written by high school teachers experienced in the original CHEM Study program. The Prentice-Hall curriculum package consists of a Student Text, Lab Manual, Teachers Guide, Achievement Tests, Audio-Visual material and special equipment.

The procedure used by the CHEM Study Steering Committee represents one way of going about improving the textbook offerings in a subject field. A tested model and feedback data are released to a publisher with the opportunity for him to develop an improved version in both subject matter and conditions for learning.

II. Chemical Systems (CBA Chemistry)

In June of 1957 a group of chemists and high school chemistry teachers met on the Reed College campus in Portland, Oregon. They met at the request of the American Chemical Society to consider ways of correlating college and high school chemistry. The committee noted there had been few changes in high school chemistry textbooks since 1920 although there had been major changes in the field of chemistry. The discussions led to a high school chemistry course written with the primary purpose of preparing students for the further study of chemistry in college. A writing committee of nine college professors and nine high school teachers of chemistry met in 1958 and 1959 to consider and to write a college preparatory chemistry course. Arthur F. Scott, Reed College, was the first director of the project, and later Laurence E. Strong of Earlham became director.

The CBA committee wanted to develop a new course that might serve to close the gap between high school and the college teaching of chemistry. This meant developing an introductory course presenting modern chemistry at the level of a high school student. Hopefully the course would bring students close to the frontiers of chemical knowledge. The major goals of chemical education were defined as follows:

1. To present the basic principles of chemistry as an intellectual discipline and to achieve an appreciation of chemistry as a creative pursuit of human knowledge.
2. To develop facility in analytical, critical thinking—especially thinking which involves logical and quantitative relations.
3. To develop scientifically literate citizens through an understanding of (a) the methods of science and (b) the role of chemistry in society and everyday living.
4. To stimulate an interest in chemistry, to identify promising students, and to provide adequate preparation for further scientific studies.

These goals express a strong humanistic orientation and represent a move away from the notion of chemistry as a practical art. The authors also preferred to develop a course oriented to critical thinking and to the appreciation of chemistry as the pursuit of knowledge. This is in contrast to conventional courses where the emphasis has been more on memorizing physical and chemical properties of elements and the accumulation of an encyclopedic assortment of information about chemical compounds and manufacturing processes.

More specifically the objectives of CBA are:

1. To understand the possibilities of fitting ideas and observations together to suggest new possibilities. This will require knowing how to use one's imagination to develop ideas. The role of the model in chemistry, its limitations and evolution is particularly important.
2. To stimulate student thought and inquiry along the lines which chemists have found useful for much of their own

productive thinking. This will require knowing how experimental data and imaginative ideas are used to further an understanding of chemical systems.
3. To have students construct a line of argument, to raise critical questions, and to recognize and account for sources of error. This will require laboratory work that provides an opportunity for relating thoughts, ideas, and experimentation.

It will be recognized from the goals and objectives there is more attention devoted to the intellectual and theoretical aspects of chemistry than is typical of conventional introductory chemistry courses.

With the educational purposes defined the CBA committee proceeded to develop a chemistry course to fit these demands. A trial edition was written in 1959, used experimentally in nine high schools and with 800 students during 1959–60. On the basis of feedback from teachers and students, the course was rewritten, and in the second trial year (1960–61) it was tested by 190 teachers and 15,000 students. The final version of the course, published by Webster Division of McGraw-Hill Book Company, represented the work of twenty authors and a preliminary testing by 300 teachers and 20,000 students.

The authors of the CBA materials followed the current efforts of chemists to organize their subject into a comprehensive conceptual system, and chose for the CBA course the theme of the chemical bond. This theme runs throughout the course and is used as the principal explanatory system—"since the making and breaking of these links *is* chemistry." Concepts of energy changes and reaction mechanisms, in addition to understanding chemical bonds, provide the core of the course. The motivation behind this new approach is to have a means for distilling the essence of what is chemistry from the enormous amount of information that has been generated by chemists. All topics in the course are closely integrated; the student is required to use ideas and information acquired earlier in the course to reach new levels of understanding later. What is learned later in the course is used to bring new meaning to information presented earlier.

The CBA laboratory program serves the conceptual design and organization of the course. There is an underlying emphasis upon "thinking about" experiments in terms of the problem to be investigated, the question for which experimental data are needed, and the role of theory, models, and concepts for interpreting data. Laboratory and class work are seen as interrelated parts of scientific inquiry and are not sharply distinguished. The emphasis is upon how humans arrive at understanding and how they develop insight. Students are not asked to do experiments which merely demonstrate what they already know. Neither are they expected to get a 'right' answer. They are required to carry out an experimental procedure, to think and plan in advance of going into the laboratory and to be intellectually involved with their observations. Laboratory experiments early in the course develop essential techniques which later are used to suggest experimental approaches to new problems. As the student becomes proficient in experimentation and as he builds his understanding of chemical systems, he reaches a place in the course where problems are presented in the laboratory without written directions. The student is expected to devise his own procedure for working on the problem. The teacher's task is to help and encourage the student to be an investigator of chemical systems rather than simply a spectator.

The instructional resources for teaching the CBA course consist of a textbook and laboratory manual for the student, and a guide to each of these for the teacher.

The textbook, *Chemical Systems,* is divided into five parts plus supporting chapters for each part; these are: 1) the nature of chemical change; 2) electrical nature of chemical systems; 3) models: aids to the interpretation of systems; 4) bonds in chemical systems; 5) order, disorder and change. The emphasis throughout is upon concepts, imaginative ideas, and models for interpreting the facts and observations of experimental work in chemistry. At the end of each section of the text there is a comprehensive review of the section with further interpretations based upon the student's newly acquired background in chemistry up to this point. These reviews also provide a link with what is to follow. At the end of each chapter there are additional student exercises written at different levels of sophistication.

Investigating Chemical Systems, is the student laboratory manual for CBA chemistry. The investigations in the manual are of three types: 1) developing basic laboratory techniques and experimental data; 2) amplifying and interpreting topics in the text; 3) carrying out an investigation from a problem statement. Directions for carrying out the experiments are minimal or lacking depending upon the background of experience the student is expected to have acquired.

TABLE 1
Recommended Film Sequence for the CBA Course

Title	Section	Source
Crystals and Crystal Growing	2–12	PSSC
Gases and How They Combine	3–5	CHEM
Electrochemical Cells	4–5	CHEM
Coulomb's Law	5–13	PSSC
Energy and Work	5–15	PSSC
Mass of the Electron	6–6	PSSC
Elementary Charge and the Transfer of Kinetic Energy	6–9	PSSC
Rutherford Atom	6–10	PSSC
Neutron, The Heart of Matter	6–13	PSSC
Chemical Bonding	7–4	CHEM
Gas Pressure and Molecular Volume	8–4	PSSC
Behavior of Gases	8–15	PSSC
Molecular Spectroscopy	8–23	CHEM
High Temperature Research	9–10	CHEM
Franck-Hertz Experiment	10	PSSC
Ionization Energy	10–9	CHEM
Research Problem—Inert Gas Compounds	10–15	CHEM
Quantum Theory—The Hydrogen Atom	10–10	CHEM
Chemical Families	10–16	CHEM
Transuranium Elements	10–16	CHEM
Crystals and Their Structures	12	CHEM
Shapes and Polarities of Molecules	13–9	CHEM
Equilibrium	15	CHEM
Catalysis	17	CHEM
Introduction to Reaction Kinetics	17	CHEM

The *Teacher's Guide* is keyed to each chapter of the student textbook and includes these sections: 1) a review of the subject matter emphasizing the major ideas and concepts; 2) a concise summary of each section of the chapter; 3) a discussion of the relationship of the chapter to the major goals of the course and describing the strategy of the chapter in relation to the objectives; 4) hints and suggestions for teaching the topics of the chapter; 5) a description of relevant demonstrations; 6) lists of student exercises in the textbook with answers and solutions.

The *Teacher's Laboratory Guide* contains: 1) directions for preparing solutions; 2) suggestions for dispensing reagents and equipment; 3) ideas for conducting the pre- and post-laboratory sessions; 4) kinds of questions students usually raise in this section of the work; 5) information for diagnosing and helping students who are having difficulties in the laboratory; 6) alternative procedures for stated experiments; 7) answers to questions in the student's laboratory manual; 8) extensions to the stated experiments; and 9) references for each experiment to be found in scientific journals or books.

The CBA does not have a film program of its own but makes use of films selected from the PSSC and CHEM Study series (Table 1).

These two new chemistry courses, CHEM and CBA, are different in their approach to the subject but in some ways are quite similar. Their similarities are:

1. They emphasize the principles underlying chemical structure, combination and energy.
2. They establish systematic relations between experiment and theory.
3. They introduce ideas in a tentative fashion and examine them in the light of experimentally derived data.
4. They have an overall internal logical structure for the textbook which makes sampling the book dangerous.
5. They insist upon the value of speculative questions and discussions as a means of promoting and sustaining motivation.
6. They require an inquiry environment in the classroom, and teachers who are heuristically inclined.

PHYSICS

Physics was a part of the curriculum of the first public high school to open in America in 1821. The first major effort to improve physics teaching was in 1886 when Harvard College established a requirement for admission of forty prescribed laboratory experiments, known as the *Harvard Descriptive List of Experiments*. At the turn of the Twentieth Century most students who graduated from high school had had a course in physics. Since 1900 the percentage of students enrolled in physics has dropped at an alarming rate. Efforts to slow the trend have been numerous and, for the most part, have consisted of attempts to increase the appeal of the course to students by making it more practical. We have had periods of toy physics, household physics, consumer physics, air-age physics, and more recently a curriculum rich in modern technology—atomic reactors, heat engines, transitors, space probes, radar, particle accelerators, electrical appliances and similar topics. For the most part the physics relevant to these developments is traditionally presented in a terse descriptive fashion accompanied by several mathematical problems to solve. Little internal coherence or logical order to the course exists and sections may be shifted around at will without damaging what is taught. Much local curriculum revision in physics has simply been a rearrangement of the traditional topics and experiments without essentially changing anything. Except for updating technological applications, the subject matter and organization of physics courses has remained essentially unchanged for the past fifty years.

Physical Science Study Committee (PSSC Physics)

The effort to improve the teaching of physics was the first venture in the science curriculum reform movement. Committee discussions began in 1956, and the thinking and events following these deliberations have had considerable influence upon other science curriculum improvement projects. The 1956 conference was held at the Massachusetts Institute of Technology and the discussions were led by Jerrold R. Zacharias, a professor of physics at M.I.T. Representatives from four universities and one research laboratory brought the results of staff discussion within their institutions and several groups had tentative outlines for a new high school physics course. There was a consensus that the traditional physics course: 1) was out of date by a half century; 2) was so overloaded with details it could not possibly be adequately taught in one year; 3) was without unity or conceptual structure, simply a patchwork of topics; and 4) was dominated by technology to the extent the science of physics was obscured. Agreement was reached in the 1956 conference on the broad outline for a new physics course and the major pedagogical characteristics it should have.

In the summer of 1957 a staff of fifty people was assembled to begin work on the new course. High school and college physics teachers made up most of the group but there were also specialists in testing, film making and educational administration. The diversity of the group was to make it possible to work on all parts of the program at once: textbook, laboratory experiments and equipment, teacher's guide, tests, films, and a "Science Study Series." A preliminary version of the textbook and laboratory manual was prepared and tested in eight schools (300 pupils) during the 1957–58 school year. Institute programs for educating teachers of the new course began in the summer of 1958. The course was rewritten to be tested again during the 1958–59 school year, this time with 270 teachers and 11,000 pupils. A third revision of the PSSC materials, based upon feedback from the 1958–59 teachers, was taught to 22,500 students by 560 teachers during the 1959–60 school year. A final version of the course was submitted to a publisher, D. C. Heath and Company, Boston, in 1960. Seven hundred and fifty people, exclusive of service and support personnel, were members of the PSSC curriculum team between 1956 and 1960. A second edition of the textbook and laboratory manual were published by the same company in 1965.

The nature of a course revision is obviously determined by the purposes physics teaching is to serve in schools. To the physicists, physics is the most exact and fundamental of the sciences. It is a highly imaginative intellectual structure of concepts and theories that provides a meaningful model of man's experience in his efforts to understand natural phenomena. In the sense that physics is a product of the creative endeavors of man's thinking, physics has the characteristics of a humanity. The PSSC committee sought to develop a high school course in physics having the qualities of physics as they are known to physicists. The educational goals set for the PSSC project were: 1) to present physics as a logically unified subject and an ever-changing search for order; 2) to demonstrate the interplay between experiment and theory; 3) to have students be active participants in learning by interrogating nature itself; in this way they learn not only the concepts and laws of physics but the evidence that supports them and its limitations; 4) to improve the student's skill in learning through the ability to read and reason critically; 5) to provide a sound foundation in high school for those students who plan to study science or engineering in college. The PSSC committee did not feel these to be the goals of the traditional high school physics course.

Inherent in the PSSC course are the following specific objectives as they are defined in terms of student accomplishment:

1. understands the place of science in society: recognizes physics as a cultural element which provides a frame of reference for interpreting many social, political and economic problems.
2. understands physics as a human activity, a product of human thought and imagination, comparable in significance with the humanities.

3. appreciates the intellectual, aesthetic and historical background of physics.
4. appreciates the limitations of knowledge about the physical world: understands physics is a science of approximations seeking always to reduce the magnitude of the approximations.
5. understands that the knowledge of physics arises from observation and experimentation, and appreciates the meaning and spirit of scientific inquiry.
6. recognizes that an activity of science is the building of models and theories; the laboratory investigation may serve as a means for testing or for generating models and theories.
7. appreciates the logical unity of physics and the special way in which the physicist thinks about and interprets the natural world.
8. understands the basic principles of physics that manifest themselves again and again in the astronomical as well as the human and atomic scales.

The goals and objectives of PSSC suggest a subject matter somewhat different from conventional courses in physics. Two major themes provide a structure for the course, these are: 1) dynamics of particles under the influence of forces and the conservation laws of momentum and energy; and 2) the superposition principle governing all wave propagation. These themes are supported by some thirty-five major concepts of physics. Special attention is given to demonstrating the interplay between experiment and theory.

The PSSC textbook contains less factual information than conventional texts, concentrating instead on a few selected concepts that have the widest explanatory power or the most intellectual 'mileage.' The committee did seek to conserve some of the traditional topics of physics but chose not to teach them. This was accomplished by developing a series of over fifty paperback monographs of about 150 pages each on such topics as crystals, weather, music, accelerators, magnets and physics-related topics in biology and chemistry. In this way it was possible to give the textbook a unified approach to physics without the distraction of technological developments in the same context.

The instructional materials for the PSSC physics course consist of a textbook of four parts and thirty-four supporting chapters. *Part I* deals with basic concepts fundamental to the study of physics: time, distance, motion, the nature of measurement, the atomic structure of matter and molecular chemistry. *Part II* is a study of optics and waves; reflection and refraction; particle theory as a possible explanation of light followed by the wave model as a possible explanation of optical phenomena. *Part III* presents the study of motion, using laboratory work to develop Newton's laws of motion; the story of gravitation follows; then the laws of conservation of momentum and energy are introduced, leading to the development of the kinetic theory of gases. *Part IV* introduces the student to electricity and magnetism; electrical forces and then measurement; the magnetic field around a current; Coulomb's Law; energy and motion of changes in an electric field; and a thorough study of the structure of atoms and related phenomena. The sequencing of the course is such as to make it possible to expand and reinterpret topics as the student's background in physics develops. The PSSC writers assumed students would have a knowledge of geometry and algebra and that any additional mathematics could be developed in the teaching of the course.

The *laboratory guide* consists of fifty-one experiments specially selected to be supportive of and to help in developing the concepts found in the textbook. It provides an introduction to experiments, gives technical hints, raises questions, but leaves the student with the opportunity to think his way through the problem. Experiments are not used to confirm an assertion but to provide a direct non-verbal contact with relevant data which become useful when analyzed. The student is led to recognize that experiments are the results of ideas as well as generators of ideas.

PSSC *laboratory equipment* is for the most part specially designed to be simple, easily assembled, and inexpensive. There has been a deliberate attempt to subordinate the equipment to the ideas underlying the experiment. This is accomplished by using everyday materials, such as, rollerskate carts, doorbell timers, and ripple tanks, which can frequently be found or made at home. The new apparatus and all equipment for the course is available, either in kits or as individual pieces, from scientific supply houses. It is estimated that it costs only ten to fifteen per cent as much to equip a laboratory to teach PSSC physics as it did for traditional courses.

The PSSC *film program* was planned from the onset of the project to serve the overall course goals. The films serve several purposes, one of which is to show experiments not possible within a classroom. In addition, the committee wanted to show physicists at work so students might see the variety of activities carried on by physicists.

To this end the films use only 'authentic' physicists and there are different people for most films. The films are distributed by *Modern Learning Aids,* New York.

PSSC *transparencies* are available for use in reviewing the mathematics required in the course and for illustrating three dimensional objects. Overlays and color are used to add perspective to the presentations.

A series of separate instructional units titled *Advanced Topics* have been developed to provide materials for students who want an extra semester of physics and to challenge students with a special interest in physics. Some of the titles in the series are: 1) angular momentum and its conservation; 2) relativistic kinematics; 3) speed, energy, and mass; and 4) atomics. These units provide new problems on the topics, alternative solutions, and additional laboratory experiments. There is a laboratory guide for each of the *Advanced Topics*. Copies of the units and guides are available from D. C. Heath and Company, Boston.

The *Teacher's Resource Book and Guide* for PSSC consists of four paperbound volumes, one for each of the four parts of the textbook. The purpose of the guide is to help teachers translate the PSSC materials into class and laboratory programs. To this end the *Guide* 1) gives concrete suggestions for class and laboratory activities; 2) identifies individual topics in the perspective of the purposes and content of the entire course; 3) discusses course topics, but at the teacher's level rather than the student's; 4) suggests the appropriate experiments, demonstrations, films, books, and other materials for each chapter; 5) provides detailed information on laboratory experiments, including lists of apparatus, purposes, optimum time, answers to questions in the student's *Laboratory Guide* and related information; 6) suggests a time schedule for teaching the course; and 7) describes the *Home, Desk and Lab* problems, with background information and the solution to each problem. For each section of the course the Guide stresses the purpose, emphasis, content, development, and provides additional comments.

There is a set of PSSC *tests* covering each section of the textbook and two comprehensive examinations available from the Cooperative Test Division of Educational Testing Service, New Jersey. These tests have been prepared: 1) to provide evidence on how well the course goals and objectives are being achieved; 2) to indicate to students the kind of learning expected of them; 3) to evaluate student performance; and 4) to indicate the student's ability to apply the knowledge and techniques he has learned to new situations.

The *Science Study Series* is a supplementary reading program to accompany PSSC physics although the books would be useful in connection with science courses in general. The books are paperback, average about 150 pages in length, and are inexpensive. Over fifty titles are available from the publisher, Doubleday and Company. One of the books, *Using the Science Study Series,* provides information on each volume in the series and a correlation chart for use with most high school physics books. Each book is written by a distinguished author. Some of the books are biographical in nature, others describe the role of science in the world of man; some provide supplementary reading, and others meet the individual tastes and interests of different students.

The PSSC curriculum project from its inception had in mind not only the development of a course new in educational concept, but the production of an entire range of instructional materials and teaching aids compatible with the course. The Physical Science Study Committee recognizes the need for a continuing revision of the curriculum as advancements in physics and pedagogy make their appearance.

The teaching of physics in the United States has a long tradition and so does the nature of the curriculum. In recent years as the enrollment in the subject has declined, several attempts have been made to find the cause. Usually these endeavors arrive at the following speculations: teachers of physics are more poorly educated than teachers in other subjects; students are badly prepared in mathematics; school counselors do not recommend the course to students; physics is a 'hard' course and to take it jeopardizes one's chances of getting into college. On the other hand, physics teachers have the brightest students, the smallest classes, and the most expensive equipment to work with. It is true the physics teacher, due to the small enrollment, has to teach other subjects. Most frequently he teaches the advanced mathematics courses prerequisite to physics. But it appears the one question seldom examined is the character of the curriculum and its suitability for general education. The Physical Science Study Committee did this and felt that if high school physics resembled more the physics which physicists prefer, high school students would enjoy it more. Ten years of curriculum experimentation along this line, while making significant contributions to course design, has demonstrated this is not the way to appeal to the interests of most high school students.

PROJECT PHYSICS

In 1962 a series of discussions began at Harvard University about the need for a new approach to the teaching of physics at the high school and junior college levels. A year later the National Science Foundation supported a conference to explore the desirability of alternative approaches to physics teaching.[5] The consensus of the twenty-six conference members, twenty-five physicists and one mathematician, was that it would be desirable to develop alternative approaches to physics teaching designed to attract a larger number of students. One of the resolutions recorded contained the following suggestions for a new course. It should 1) be sound physics; 2) have close connections with other sciences, such as, astronomy and chemistry; 3) illustrate the methodological and historical development of the sciences; and 4) include the social and cultural consequences of the progress of science. These recommendations supported the earlier thinking of the committee at Harvard.

In 1964, the Harvard group began the development of a new physics course along the lines they had been discussing. Support for the program came from the Carnegie Corporation, the Alfred P. Sloan Foundation, the U.S. Office of Education, and the National Science Foundation. The title of this curriculum venture was simply *Project Physics.*

The twelve man Advisory Committee for Project Physics included college physicists, high school physics teachers, chemists, historians of science, a mathematician, philosophers of science, science educators, and a specialist in publishing and one in scientific manpower problems. Three co-directors for the program were appointed: Gerald Holton, a physicist and philosopher of science; Fletcher G. Watson, a science educator in the Harvard Graduate School of Education and an astronomer; and F. James Rutherford, a high school physics teacher and a member of the Harvard Graduate School of Education. This unique arrangement of co-directors provided the

[5] *Proceedings of the Ad Hoc Advisory Conference on Secondary School Physics.* Oct. 31-Nov. 1963, National Science Foundation, Washington, D.C. (Mimeo).

variety of expertise particularly suitable for a high school science curriculum development project. Within the next several years some eighty additional specialists were added to the project staff including physicists, high school teachers, test and evaluation experts, and film makers.

Traditionally high school physics has been a college preparatory course. In 1900 almost all who graduated from high school had had a physics course, and most went to college. By 1969 fewer than one in five of the high school graduates took physics, and most did so to meet a college entrance requirement. The developers of Project Physics were of the opinion all students should have physics to understand modern society. They also felt a course different in kind from either PSSC or traditional physics was required to enlist the interest of a substantial number of students. In other words, it must be a general education course built upon 'good' physics and designed for today's educated citizen. Gerald Holton has spoken of 'good' physics as having a "continuous inherent story line." It is not a panorama of details or pieces easy to teach; it is not 'soft' or made up of everyday technological applications. It is related to human endeavor within a cultural component; it reveals the structure of physics and provides an "encompassing view of the workings of nature." It is a course with a historical and philosophical sense presenting a coherent view of physics.

The directors of Project Physics not only wanted to develop a new approach to physics teaching but at the same time to improve upon the science curriculum designs which emerged during the early 1960's. Specifically they planned 1) to recognize more the role of the teacher; 2) to consider the range of academic interests and abilities among students; 3) to recognize what is feasible to do in schools; 4) to accept the responsibility of detailed formative and summative evaluation; 5) to incorporate the advantages of a multimedia approach to learning; and 6) to establish a closer working relationship and cooperation between schools, colleges, teacher education institutions and the teachers in high schools and universities. Furthermore, the committee wished to: 1) develop a tested physics course for use on a national basis as an alternative to other available courses; 2) include content not prominent in most courses but widely held to be desirable; 3) incorporate the best of pedagogic procedures to meet the interests of a wide range of students and of physics teachers with diverse backgrounds; 4) provide teachers with the necessary aids to teach physics under realistic conditions of time and classroom situations; 5) provide a means for using the new technology of education; 6) evolve a program recognizing the role of the teacher and the involvement of the student in obtaining a greater diversity and flexibility within a curriculum. Through these efforts it was hoped enrollments in physics would increase and physics would be of value to students seeking a general education as well as those with a pre-professional interest.

We have explored the objectives of Project Physics in some detail because it represents a new approach to curriculum development in science, one that may well set the new direction in the 1970's. It will be noted the curriculum developers have sought to validate their course in terms of 1) the discipline of physics; 2) a philosophical position about the values of physics; 3) learning effectiveness and differentiated learning; 4) teacher and instructional effectiveness; and 5) a consideration of the physics course in relation to the total curriculum. The range of curriculum and teaching criteria considered in Project Physics is unique among new science teaching programs. The developers have sought to go beyond the 1960 ideological setting for curriculum improvement.

The educational objectives of Project Physics are to have young people understand and appreciate: 1) how the basic facts, principles and ideas of modern physics developed; 2) who made the key contributions and something of the lives of the men and women who did; 3) scientific methodology as illustrated by physics; 4) how physics relates to the cultural and economic aspects of contemporary society; 5) the effect of physics on other sciences, especially chemistry and astronomy; and 6) the relationship and interaction between physics and contemporary technology. The setting of these goals is within a solid background of 'good' physics and the perspective of man's intellectual and cultural heritage. Although the course stresses the facts, concepts, and theories of physics, it is equally concerned with the methods by which the knowledge of physics grows. Students are expected to understand the nature of the scientific enterprise as well as the social consequences of science. This humanistic approach to physics teaching emphasizes human values and meaning in the light of contemporary physics.

Course Development

The first draft of Project Physics was written and taught experimentally in two high schools during the 1963–64 school year. The course was rewritten and supplementary materials were developed during the summer of 1964. These were tested in sixteen high schools and one junior college, involving 550 students in 1964–65. Further developments were made and the newly revised form of Project Physics materials were taught in 1965–66 by fifty-four teachers. The third draft version, 1966–67, was taught to 2,500 students. In 1967–68, further revisions and testing of the materials were carried out in 100 schools, involving 200 classes and 4,000 students. During 1967–68 nine schools and 500 students were selected as controls for use in the evaluation study of Project Physics. In the sample of 100 test schools for 1967–68 were fifty teachers selected randomly from among the 16,000 high school physics teachers of the United States. These teachers taught the materials for the first time and helped answer questions about how realistic the new physics program was for the typical teacher, school, and pupil. The 1967–68 materials were again revised, the text was shortened, and new instructional materials were added to make up an *interval edition* for schools to use during the 1968–69 school year. The final edition of the text and all ancillary materials will be commercially available early in 1970 in time for a critical examination by science staffs who may wish to consider the adoption of the materials for the 1970–71 school year. All printed, projected, and laboratory materials of the project will be available from Holt, Rinehart and Winston, Inc., New York. The four revisions of the texts, laboratory and experimental guides have been based upon feedback from students and teachers, and an on-going evaluation program developed by the staff to assess progress toward the goals of the program. For example, it has been found that physics enrollments tend to increase an average of thirty per cent in schools using Project Physics more than one year; this was one purpose for developing the course.

Course Materials

The *Student Guides* or 'textbook' for Project Physics in its experimental form is divided into six units, each of which is intended to occupy a class for one to two months. The units are: 1) Concepts of Motion; 2) Motion in the Heavens; 3) Energy; 4) Waves and Fields; 5) Models of the Atom; and 6) The Nucleus. Beginning with concepts of motion, one unit provides a grounding for the study of motion in the heavens. This forms a basis for a study of the conservation laws in Unit III. The fourth unit presents electricity and magnetism in the context of fields at rest and in motion. Units V and VI present the origins of the new physics and introduce the atomic and nuclear models of matter. There is a Prologue to each unit providing a historical, cultural, or philosophical perspective to the topics, and an Epilogue which summarizes their relevance to what is to follow.

In developing the text the authors have sought to: 1) focus on a few basic ideas, themes, or fundamental laws and to avoid lengthy deviations; 2) maintain a 'story-line' in a sequence of related ideas illustrating the persistence of great themes in physics; 3) keep mathematics to a level consistent with a fair but basic presentation of the subject matter; 4) regulate the rate at which new concepts are introduced, then to consolidate relevant concepts at intervals; 5) provide a coherent articulated course tying the six units together; 6) include topics that are so significant as to be useful repeatedly in the course. History is used in each unit not for the sake of history but as a pedagogic aid, to illustrate the characteristics of physics which have made it preeminent in the history of ideas. The basic core of units is arranged to provide many 'handles' by which a student may relate physics to his own interests and concerns. The identification of the "textbook" as a *Student Guide* is done deliberately to indicate there are other sources of information in the course in addition to the "text."

As an additional resource for studying physics a series of *supplementary units* are being developed. Some of the titles are: 1) Discoveries in Physics; 2) Elementary Particles; and 3) Maxwell's Electromagnetic Theory. About twenty units are planned covering a wide range of physics and related topics. This will make it possible for the teacher to choose options he feels are important for a physics course as well as provide a means for meeting the special interests of students. These and other components of Project Physics are matched so as not to destroy the integration of the course.

A dozen or so *self-instruction booklets* consisting of programed lessons on special topics have been written. Among the titles are: 1) The Nature of Vectors; 2) Adding Vectors; 3) Components of Vectors; 4) Kinetic-Molecular Theory; 5) Electrical Fields and Forces; 6) Energy Level Diagrams; 7) Bohr's Theory of the Hydrogen Atom; and 8) a series on Waves. These programs were written to serve as an alternative to problem solving, as an introduction to physical concepts, and as a supplement to laboratory exercises. Two broad purposes are served by these booklets: to present adjunct materials not covered in the textbook; and help weaker students in understanding concepts used in the course. In both areas the booklets are designed to assist the student in learning how to learn, not merely to provide answers or a means for drill. There are more programed materials for the early units of the course than for the last half.

There are seven *Physics Readers* for Project Physics, one to accompany each of the teaching units and one entitled *About Science,* containing more general and philosophical articles not belonging specifically within any one unit. The *Reader* is not intended as a textbook. It is a series of outstanding articles and book passages on various aspects of physics that relate to a particular teaching unit. The collection is intended for browsing and to accommodate the special interests of students. Within each booklet one finds a balance of science articles: a few are on historic events, others explain what physicists do, some discuss the philosophy of science, several describe discoveries, and still others deal with the impact of scientific thought on various human activities. There are old and new classics, but all are selected for the interest they may arouse, for their relevance, and for their quality. A brief resume or excerpt of each article is found in the teacher's guide.

The *Project Physics Handbooks* are student guides, one for each of the six units of the course. These handbooks are unique in science teaching. They are intended to acquaint the student with all the learning resources available to him in his study of a unit—information usually known only to the teacher. The *Handbook* describes experiments to be done, with a discussion of each. A series of related activities include additional experiments, suggested readings, recommended film loops, and review problems. The appendix contains data tables, references to the Reader, and useful supplementary information. The *Handbook* represents another way of reminding the student about the sources of learning input available to him from which he can make choices.

One of the instructional components of Project Physics is the *Laboratory Guide*. In each of the six units of the course are four or five experiments loosely related to the textbook. Of the forty-eight experiments in the course twenty-four are identified as basic and twenty-four represent extensions of the same topics. A teacher has the option of a strongly based laboratory program or one that is adequate. In the student's *Laboratory Guide* each experiment is briefly described, with cautions concerning the proper use of the equipment, and suggestions for further inquiry. Some experiments are intended to familiarize students with a topic, to help them 'get the feeling.' These do not require measurements nor is a 'write-up' recommended. Others are quantitative in nature, beginning with a question and requiring a mathematical interpretation or prediction from experimental observations. At other times the laboratory experiments require a series of observations over a long period of time. Some experiments are of a discovery nature while others are used to verify known physical activities. Many of the experiments are suitable as teacher or student demonstrations. Whether the lab precedes, parallels, or follows the class discussion is determined by its pedagogic purpose. Some examples of the laboratory exercises are: 1) uniform motion; 2) trajectories; 3) variations in data; 4) the orbit of Mars; 5) collisions in one dimension; 6) random events; 7) sound; 8) electrolysis; 9) introduction to waves; and 10) radioactive tracers. The experiments in Project Physics are designed to serve one or more of the following purposes: 1) provide firsthand experience with phenomena; 2) promote interest and encourage question asking; 3) introduce, discover, or extend physical concepts; 4) illustrate the central role of experimentation and measurement in physics; and 5) develop a theoretical model and show how it can be used and modified by putting predictions to a test. The fullest meaning of an experiment is developed by asking both qualitative and quantitative questions of the student.

The *laboratory equipment* for Project Physics is in part newly designed and the remainder is standard. The eighty or so equipment items are largely of a modular type making it possible for the components to be combined or rearranged to serve different purposes. This not only reduces costs but also helps the student become familiar with its possible uses. Several experiments can be carried out with the same equipment and it can be used for demonstrations. The cost for equipping a Project Physics laboratory would be approximately one-third to one-half less than for other programs.

The 8 mm. *film loop* is an integral part of the instructional program of Project Physics. About 200 of these single concept color films are planned and more than fifty are now available. The majority of the film loops are quantitative or semi-quantitative, from which students can obtain measurements of significant physical quantities. In this way the student is interacting with the film rather than passively watching it. Slow motion is used where helpful for making observations. Wherever possible, scenes familiar to the student outside of the laboratory are used to convey the idea physics extends beyond the classroom. Not only do these loops serve a laboratory function, but many introduce, illustrate, or summarize a concept; others have been constructed to serve as quiz items. Detailed notes accompany each of the films. Titles of some of the film loops are: 1) Models of the Atom; 2) Inertial Forces on an Elevator; 3) Explosion of a Cluster of Objects; 4) The Four-Minute Mile; 5) Photon Interference; and 6) Retrograde Motion of a Plant—two films, one of which illustrates the Ptolemaic Model and the other the Current Model. These film loops are distributed by The Ealing Corporation, Cambridge, Massachusetts.

The 16 mm. *sound film* program of Project Physics is planned to contribute to the diverse goals of the course. Good existing films on physics made by other projects or commercial houses are identified in the Teacher's Guide. New films are being produced for use in Project Physics on topics not usually available on film, such as, the historical and social aspects of physics. One film in the series, for example, is a documentary film about experimental physicists at work on a 'real' investigation. The film is entitled *People and Particles* and concentrates on the many people and their activities in investigating electron-positron pair production. The daily activities of the people involved in the experiment were recorded over several months of time on 50,000 feet of film. The film was then cut to less than 1,500 feet. A guide has been written to supplement the film and describe its use. The producers feel the film should be shown early in the year to stimulate student discussions about research. At a second showing near the end of the year students will be in a position to discuss the physical principles represented in the film. The film guide has been arranged in parts to facilitate a different discussion at each showing. A documentary film on the life of Enrico Fermi is planned.

To assist in presenting topics in Project Physics *overhead projector transparencies* have been developed and their potential for teaching physics explored. The transparencies are multicolored with overlays, and in some cases can be used to simulate motion. Among their features are: 1) the projection of accurate drawings or diagrams; 2) the use of overlays to analyze the significant features of a picture; and 3) the presentation of scaled versions of incidents from loop films. They can also be used as one means for quizzing students. The set of transparencies for any unit is described in the Teacher's Guide and possible uses discussed.

The entire assortment of teaching materials for Project Physics represent a 'systems' approach to teaching. All the materials represent various media for presenting physics; furthermore, they are coordinated and integrated in a way to reinforce the effectiveness of any one media. The range of materials makes it possible for the teacher to build a teaching 'package' in a way he finds most useful, knowing all the instructional components are compatible with the philosophy of the program and other teaching materials.

The *Teacher Guide* for Project Physics describes all the materials available for the course and keys them into their proper place in the student text. There is a separate guide for each of the six course units. These are among the ways the *Guide* assists the teacher: 1) provides background on unfamiliar areas, such as, the history and philosophy of science; 2) shows how teaching media are related conceptually; 3) suggests possible teaching schedules on a day-to-day basis; 4) extensively discusses laboratory experiments and demonstrations; 5) suggests alternate experiments and demonstrations; 6) shows one way a lesson may be developed; 7) lists equipment needs for the day; 8) provides answers to problems with a discussion; and 9) suggests additional resources, such as, student and teacher references to books and articles (these are coded as to suitability). A series of training films are under development to provide pre- and in-service education for the teaching of Project Physics.

The *mode of teaching* required for Project Physics is indicated by the goals of the course and the nature of the instructional materials. It is quite evident desirable teaching operations demand a climate of inquiry in the classroom, under conditions favorable to a maximum interaction between students and a well-trained teacher. The 'good' teacher of Project Physics is not only knowledgeable about physics but also about pedagogy. He understands and can use a wide range of instructional media although he may prefer one media over another. He recognizes that young people, by the time they reach high school, apparently have developed distinctive cognitive styles and certain unique interests. Project Physics has provided a system of instructional resources to accommodate this wide range of teaching and learning styles. This is done without sacrificing a sound philosophy of science teaching or degrading physics.

There are prepared *tests* for each of the six instructional units of the course. These tests consist of multiple-choice questions, problems and essay questions. The developers of Project Physics encourage teachers to use other means in addition to formal tests to evaluate student achievement. Examples are: 1) extra reading; 2) self-initiated work; 3) variations on laboratory work; 4) research papers on the history and philosophy of science; 5) critical book reviews; 6) debates and discussions on alternative points of view, such as, Ptolemaic vs. Copernican solar system, and light as waves vs. light as particles; 7) further mathematical exploration of the laws of physics; and 8) a variety of creative enterprises, such as, plays, essays, music and artistic expressions.

In addition to student testing, Project Physics has carried on an extensive program of *curriculum evaluation.* Its purposes are to provide information useful for course improvement and to assess how effective the course is in realizing the established goals under specified school conditions. The results of the latter effort are expected to furnish answers to questions eventual consumers of the program will undoubtedly wish to know. Other parts of the evaluation model involve research on teacher effectiveness, student interests, and instructional media and techniques. Preliminary results from some of the studies indicate the majority of general education students find Project Physics enjoyable and would recommend it to their friends. Students particularly liked the laboratory work.

ENGINEERING CONCEPTS CURRICULUM PROJECT

One approach to the teaching of physical science in high school might be "through technology." This was the suggestion of one group of physicists at the *Ad Hoc Advisory Conference on Secondary School Physics* called by the National Science Foundation in 1963.[6] The committee recognized the limited appeal of PSSC physics to most high school students and the strong appeal technology has for a large segment of the population. Through technology they thought a considerable number of students could be taught physical principles with a promise of understanding the world man has built. The committee recognized this would involve understanding "the operation of systems of elements which may not be individually under-

[6] See footnote No. 5, page 193.

stood in all detail but are well characterized as regards the parameters used in the system. Gears, levers, fluid-filled tubes, electronic components, are possible bases for understanding technology." The opinion of the attending physicists was that "an honest course with this content, together with the accompanying films, tools, and experiments, would provide facilities for the introduction of technological background in the earlier years and would provide an opportunity to give a valuable, flexible background to students in vocational tracks. It should be possible to use the technology of the times to bring to students an enjoyment of the scientific ideas underlying technology."

These discussions resulted in the development of a new high school course entitled *Engineering Concepts Curriculum Project* (ECCP). The project has been supported by the National Science Foundation, and the curriculum plans have been carried out by the Commission on Engineering Education. The co-directors of the program have been E. E. David, Jr. of the Bell Telephone Laboratories, Murray Hill, New Jersey, and J. G. Truxal, Polytechnical Institute of Brooklyn, New York. The Commission took note of the recommendations of the NSF Advisory Conference and proceeded under these assumptions: 1) an understanding of the nature and effect of the tools man has invented to extend the capabilities of his body and mind can tie physical principles to the man-made world; and 2) in the light of the diminishing enrollments in high school physics, a new course should be developed, one new both in content and approach. During the summer of 1967 the objectives for this new course were discussed and possible approaches to its teaching were explored. The curriculum committee of engineers and industrial scientists concluded that not only was a new course needed but it was also feasible.

The rationale underlying the new course arose from the recognition of the gap between the idealized laws of nature and the engineering devices, systems, processes, and structures found useful in today's world. Engineering is a field concerned with processes, systems, and devices to meet technical needs within economic and social constraints. As such it provides a means of bridging the gap between scientific laws and theories and human values and social needs. Much of science is taught for its own justification. The engineer, however, thinks of the world in terms of how it can be manipulated to serve man. How we *want* the world rather than the way it is. This is to say man is capable of shaping his own environment and does not need to leave his destiny to chance. *The Man-Made World* was therefore chosen as the name for the new course, reflecting the spirit of its underlying philosophy.

Several decisions made about the character of the course were these: 1) it should be a *cultural* course with technical and scientific content; 2) it should *not* be a vocational course emphasizing detailed technology and engineering skills; 3) it should not replace biology, chemistry, or physics in high school, but provide an alternative course; and 4) it should be written to interest the seventy per cent of high school graduates who do not take physics. The course is conceived as a general education course for the average college-bound youth who has two years of mathematics. Its major purpose is to acquaint students with the broad theories and techniques governing technological concepts, and the resources needed to make these useful for creating a man-made world. The developers of the course recognize the need to demonstrate the relevance of engineering concepts and physical principles for biology, economics, sociology, business, communication, psychology, the arts and humanities. This is essential if young people are to have the insights needed to cope with technical problems in a social, economic, and political context.

The educational goals for *The Man-Made World* are: 1) to contribute to the technical literacy of all students; 2) to understand the impact of technology on today's world well enough to think rationally about technically-based problems affecting society; 3) to appreciate technological-individual-societal interactions; 4) to provide insights into and understanding of the devices, processes, systems, and structures man creates to help him cope with nature; 5) to use beneficially the fruits of technology as they increasingly influence science and shape the quality of life in our society; 6) to appreciate the precision of thought and language gained through mathematics by manipulating symbols, and using models; 7) to acquire some of the basic engineering concepts and principles by means of which the world may be viewed rationally; and 8) to correct misconceptions and oversimplifications about the nature of science and of engineering. The setting for these goals is that of engineering in the modern sense and concerns the newly developed artifacts man has created to cope with nature. As one of the ECCP developers has commented: "This is a course that could not have been written twenty-five years ago."

During the summer of 1965, after some preliminary explorations and testing of a tentative program, a team of twenty-five engineers, industrial and university scientists, and high school teachers met to develop a new course based upon engineering concepts. The personnel for the writing conference were largely chosen from Bell Telephone Laboratories, International Business Machines Corporation, Polytechnical Institute of Brooklyn, Johns Hopkins University, Massachusetts Institute of Technology and other universities. They wrote *The Man-Made World* for testing in five high schools during the 1965–66 school year. The course proved to be too difficult with regard to mathematical and physical concepts. It was then modified and taught during 1966–67 in twenty-eight schools distributed over seventeen states. Using the feedback from these schools, further improvements were made in the program, including new laboratory equipment. It was again tested, this time (1967–68) in sixty-five high schools representing twenty states and including 2,000 students. The text has been further revised to improve sections found to be difficult to teach, and to include more technology and its social impact. A preliminary final version was made available for use in schools during the 1968–69 school year. The final revision will be published commercially by the McGraw-Hill Book Company. In the fall of 1969 an adaptation of the course will be made for use in junior colleges and for non-science majors in four-year colleges and universities. The student population for testing the course has been seventy-three per cent grade twelve, twenty-seven per cent grade eleven; ninety-six per cent plan to enter college; twenty-seven per cent are oriented toward careers in mathematics and science, twenty-three per cent plan on non-science-oriented professions, seventeen per cent would like to be technicians, and thirty-six per cent are undecided.

The *textbook,* in its current experimental form, has fifteen chapters organized into three parts: 1) Logic and Computers; 2) Models and Measurement; and 3) Energy and Control. The unifying theme of the course is "the extension of man's natural abilities to cope with nature." In this regard the three parts of the book may be described as 1) the extension of man's *mental powers* through information handling and processing; 2) the extension of man's *sensory powers* through information that can be used to formulate effective strategies of mobility and communication; and 3) the extension of man's *muscular powers* through the control of energy to specific ends. Supporting these themes are a number of technical concepts which have a broad relationship and significance for society. Some of these concepts are: 1) cause and effect models; 2) uncertainty and noise; 3) frequency response; 4) optimization; 5) machine logic; 6) memory; 7) data sensing and measuring; 8) models for the study of real systems; 9) amplification (control of large amounts of energy by a small amount of energy); 10) energy; 11) performance limitations set by unavoidable statistical fluctuations; 12) information as a measurable quantity; 13) stability (the tendency of a system or device to come to a steady state when it is disturbed); 14) feedback as a means for controlling performance in which effects are fed back to control cause; 15) measurement experimentation; 16) selecting a metric for making judgments or choices; and 17) organization of units into meaningful structures either conceptual or actual. These representative concepts are set in the context of use in realistic situations both technologically and socially. The earlier part of the course is essentially more nearly logic than mathematics; the remainder requires more mathematics and is dependent upon graphical and experimental techniques. Considerable attention is devoted to the digital computer as one of the most fundamental and powerful inventions of modern times. The computer is introduced as a tool used by engineers in implementing the concepts of modeling, amplification, feedback, stability, and optimization.

Some notion of the content of the course may be gleaned from the following tentative chapter titles in the order they appear in the text.

Part A—*LOGIC AND COMPUTERS*

1. Logical thought and electric circuits
2. Logic circuits with memory
3. Plan for a computer
4. Programing a computer in machine code
5. Symbolic programing

Part B—*MODELS AND MEASUREMENT*

1. Models
2. Models and the analog computer
3. Data, sensing, and measurement
4. Dynamic models
5. Optimization

Part C—*ENERGY AND CONTROL*

1. Feedback and control
2. Amplification
3. Stability
4. Energy and the art of the possible

An important part of the ECCP consists of the thirty *laboratory experiments* planned to accompany the course. These experiments require for the most part specially designed equipment. In *Part A* of the course students use a simple cardboard digital computer (CARDIAC) and a logic circuit board. In *Part B* a simplified analog computer and a theodolete is required. In the part on *Energy and Control,* a three-wheel cart is used to demonstrate stability, and a bridge on rockers with the center of rotation above, at, and below the center of curvature of the rockers. There is also need for an analog computer, oscilloscope, signal generator, mass spring system, and along with other major items an assortment of small things. Assuming one logic circuit board for every two students and one analog computer and polylab for every three in a class of twenty-four pupils, the cost for a complete laboratory package would be about $5,000 at 1969 prices. By using split laboratory sessions, the cost could be reduced to around $3,000. The *Student Laboratory Manual* has complete directions for each experiment and several associated problems. These problems call upon the student's knowledge of engineering concepts as well as some understanding of the equipment he is using. Where possible, schools are encouraged to make use of time sharing computer services via remote access terminals for regular class and laboratory work.

The *Teacher's Manual* for ECCP was written for the most part by teachers who have been involved in the program. The specific objectives for each chapter and the student prerequisites are identified. An estimated teaching time in terms of hours is given. The experiments and demonstrations that go with the chapter are described and their placement in the learning sequence noted. Also included is the hardware that will be necessary. There are suggestions about the learning materials of the chapter as well as about homework, quizzes, and tests. The major ideas to be acquired by the student are listed and background information is provided for the teacher.

The *style of teaching* for ECCP is one of involving students in problem-solving situations. About twenty-five per cent of the course time is devoted to laboratory-type problems. Every effort is made to present students with subject matter related to clearly recognizable real-world situations in the context of modern society. The course will make demands upon the teacher because most teachers of physical science have not been educated along the lines suggested by the goals of the ECCP.

A curriculum evaluation is planned for ECCP to answer questions about 1) attainment of the objectives; 2) suitability for different kinds of students and teachers; 3) requirements in terms of physical facilities and success with the program; 4) means for training teachers; and 5) relation of the ECCP course to other courses in the high school curriculum. Various testing devices will be used and control groups of students where applicable.

It should be noted that *The Man-Made World* is essentially a science course invented for inclusion in the high school program and has no previous counterpart in the curriculum. This is in contrast to the content improvement rationale underlying the other science courses in the curriculum reform.

VIII

Bibliography on Modern Science Curriculum Projects

BIOLOGY

Abraham, Norman. "The Interaction of Experiments and Ideas: A BSCS Second Course." *Journal of Research in Science Teaching,* 2:60–63, No. 1, 1964.

———. "Letters to the Editor." *American Biology Teacher,* 26:263–264, April, 1964.

"AIBS Biological Sciences Curriculum Study." [Summary of the presentation made by Walter Auffenberg] *The Bulletin of the National Association of Secondary-School Principals,* 45:191–192, April, 1961.

Amaro, A. "Considerations Upon the BSCS (Green Version)." *American Biology Teacher,* 26:347, May, 1964.

Ashton, Mark D. "Traditional and BSCS Biology." *Catholic Educational Review,* 64:190–195, March, 1966.

Ausubel, David P. "An Evaluation of the BSCS Approach to High School Biology." *American Biology Teacher,* 28:176–186, March, 1966.

Baker, J. W. "BSCS: Biology Bandwagon." (In TST Forum) *The Science Teacher,* 30:73–74, October, 1963.

"Biological Science Curriculum Study." (Film Review) *Science,* 138:21, October 5, 1962.

"Biology Education of Secondary School Pupils." *Soviet Education,* 6:36–42, October, 1964.

Blankenship, Jacob W. "Biology Teachers and Their Attitudes Concerning BSCS." *Journal of Research in Science Teaching,* 3:54–60, No. 1, 1965.

Brett, William J. "BSCS Biology." *Teacher's College Journal,* 33: 116–118, March, 1962.

Calandra, Alexander. "Foundation Sponsored Programs." (in TST Forum) *The Science Teacher,* 36:73, February, 1964.

———. "The New Science Curriculums—A Sharp Dissent." *School Management,* 8:75–82, November, 1964.

"Checklist for Evaluating a Biology Laboratory." *The Bulletin of the National Association of Secondary-School Principals,* 45: 182, November, 1961.

Colby, Edward. "The New Science Curriculums—A Loud Hurrah." *School Management,* 8:83+, November, 1964.

Cornelius, M. E. "BSCS Motivates Students." *School and Community,* 52:28–29, October, 1965.

Cox, H. T. "Modern Biology: A Unifying Science; AIBS-BSCS Versions." *Journal of Secondary Education,* 39:9–13, January, 1964.

Crossland, Richard W. "The American Biological Sciences Curriculum Study." *American Biological Teacher,* 26:348–353, May, 1964.

Davis, Jerry B. "The BSCS Program's Variable Factor." *Science Education,* 50:221–222, April, 1966.

Dawson, James R. "Impact of New Curricula on Facilities for Biology." *American Biology Teacher,* 26:601–604, December, 1964.

Defler, Donald J. "Using Closed Circuit Television with Biological Science Curriculum Studies Material." *American Biology Teacher,* 28:699–703, November, 1966.

Earle, A. H. "Review of the BSCS Second Year Course." *American Biology Teacher,* 29:295–296, April, 1967.

Ferris, Frederick L. Jr. "Testing in the New Curriculum: Numerology, 'Tyranny,' or Common Sense?" *The School Review,* 70:112–131, Spring, 1962.

Fordyce, Philip R. "The Work of the BSCS Which May Lead to Content Adjustment on the Horizon." *School Science and Mathematics,* 61:131–135, February, 1961.

Frankel, Edward. "BSCS, Where New Horizons Begin." *The Science Teacher,* 29:47+, May, 1962.

———. "A Decade of Advanced Placement Program in Biology." *American Biology Teacher,* 26:357–362, May, 1964.

Frazier, R. W. and Baker, A. J. "Quality Science for the Senior High School: The Course in Biology." *Quality Science for Secondary Schools,* Washington, D. C.: National Science Teachers Association, 1960. Pp. 88–102.

Gallentine, J. L. and Salberg, A. N. "Factors Relating to Success in Teaching Modern High School Biology." *Science Education,* 51:305–309, April, 1967.

Gardner, Marjorie H. "How to Plan and Equip for Science Education." *The Nation's Schools,* 69:61–84, March, 1962.

George, Kenneth D. "The Effect of BSCS and Conventional Biology on Critical Thinking." *Journal of Research in Science Teaching,* 3:293–299, No. 4, 1965.

Glass, H. Bentley. "Most Critical Aspect of Science Teaching." *The Science Teacher,* 34:19–23, May, 1967.

———. "Renascent Biology: A Report on the AIBS Biological Sciences Curriculum Study." *The School Review,* 70:16–50, Spring, 1962.

Grobman, Arnold. "Biology is Changing Too: Curriculum Changes at Every Level from Elementary School Through College." *Saturday Review,* 46:67+, September 21, 1963.

———. "The Responsibilities of a Critic." (in TST Forum) *The Science Teacher,* 38:64–65, November, 1963.

Grobman, Hulda. "Assignment of Students to Tracks in Biology." *American Biology Teacher,* 27:762–764, December, 1965.

———. "High School Biology: On What Grade Level Does it Belong." *Clearing House,* 38:498–499, April, 1964.

———. "How Do We Get Better Science Teaching?" *The Bulletin of the National Association of Secondary-School Principals,* 45:106–112, February, 1961.

———. "Identifying the 'Slow Learner' in BSCS High School Biology." *Journal of Research in Science Teaching,* 3:3–11, No. 1, 1965.

———. "A New Curriculum in Biological Sciences." *Educational Leadership,* 18:360–363, March, 1961.

———. "Student Performance in New Biology Programs." *Science,* 143:265–266, January 17, 1964.

———. "A Study in Educational Improvement." *The Clearing House,* 36:173–176, November, 1961.

Hughes, Phillip. "Decisions and Curriculum Design." *Educational Theory,* 12:187–192, July, 1962.

Hurd, Paul DeHart. "The New Curriculum Movement in Science." *The Science Teacher,* 29:6–9, February, 1962.

Hutto, Thomas A. "The BSCS Program: Reaction From Students, Teachers, and Parents." *School Science and Mathematics,* 65:764–767, December, 1965.

Ivo, Sister Mary, B.V.M. "The Catholic High School and the BSCS Program." *The American Biology Teacher,* 24:361–363, May, 1962.

Klinckmann, Evelyn. "New Curriculum Patterns for Biology Teachers." *The American Association of Colleges for Teacher Education Fiftieth Yearbook.* Washington, D. C.: Amer. Assoc. of Col. for Teach. Ed., 1962. Pp. 94–103.

Klinge, Paul. "Resources for Improving Instruction in Biology." *School Life,* 45:12–14, October, 1962.

Lee, Addison E. "Biology Laboratory Instruction Innovation." *The Science Teacher,* 28:464, October, 1961.

———. "The Experimental Approach in Teaching Biology." *The American Biology Teacher,* 23:409–411, November, 1961.

Lightner, Jerry P. "The BSCS and Advanced Biology." *American Biology Teacher,* 26:338–340, May, 1964.

Lisonbee, Lorenzo. "Teaching Science to the Disadvantaged Pupil." *The Science Teacher,* 30:18–21, October, 1963.

———. "Teaching Science to the Slow Learner: The BSCS Point of View." *School Science and Mathematics,* 65:39–46, January, 1965.

———, and Fullerton, Bill J. "The Comparative Effect of BSCS and Traditional Biology on Student Achievement." *School Science and Mathematics,* 64:594–598, October, 1964.

———, and Fliegler, Louis A. "The BSCS and the Slow Learner." *American Biology Teacher,* 26:334–337, May, 1964.

Little, E. *et al.* "Team Teaching Program at Nathan Hale Senior High School." *American Biology Teacher,* 28:190–192, March, 1966.

Maberly, Norman C. and Margolin, Sandra Lee. "Biology Curriculum Patterns in Twenty-Nine High Schools." *Science Education,* 49:376–377, October, 1965.

Marie, Sister Julia, O.S.F. "Teaching Biology in High School: A

Critique of the BSCS Green Version." *Catholic School Journal,* 62:46–47, October, 1962.

Martin, W. Edgar. "Planning Facilities for High School Biological Sciences." *American School Board Journal,* 145:120–124, July, 1962.

Mayer, William V. "The Impact of Testing A New Curriculum." *American Biology Teacher,* 26:585–588, December, 1964.

McKibben, Margaret J. "The Study of New Developments in Secondary School Science, Grades 7–12." *Science Education,* 45:403–409, December, 1961.

Metzner, Jerome. "The Gifted Student Program of the BSCS." *American Biology Teacher,* 26:341–344, May, 1964.

Miller, Helena A. "Proposal for the Improvement of Education in America." *American Biology Teacher,* 27:40–43, January, 1965.

Nicodemus, Robert B. "Science Curriculum Implementation: A Problem of Teachers and Schools." *Science Education,* 49:385–386, October, 1965.

Novak, Alfred and Abraham, Norman. "Excellence in Biology Facilities." *The Science Teacher,* 29:144, March, 1962.

Peterson, Glen R. *American Biology Teacher,* 28:173–175, March, 1966.

Thomas, Dempsey L. "A Suggested Teaching Schedule for Biological Science." *American Biology Teacher,* 26:354–356, May, 1964.

Tricker, R. A. R. "Impressions of the Teaching of Science in Schools in the United States of America." *School Science and Mathematics,* 62:3–21, January, 1962.

VanDeventer, W. C. "BSCS Materials in the Preparation of Teachers of Biology." *School Science and Mathematics,* 64:683–693, November, 1964.

Voss, B. E. "Impact of BSCS Biology." *School Science and Mathematics,* 67:145–148, February, 1967.

Walsh, G. A. and Kelly, W. P. "BSCS in the Yellow Version." *Catholic School Journal,* 63:47–49, October, 1963.

Walsh, John. "Curriculum Reform: Success Hasn't Spoiled NSF Program But Biology Study's Status Reflects Problems." *Science,* 149:280–282, July 16, 1965.

Weaver, Richard L. "BSCS Plus." *American Biology Teacher,* 25:404, October, 1963.

Weishar, William J. and Terry, Richard E. "Our First Year Under BSCS." *American Biology Teacher,* 26:345–346, May, 1964.

Wilson, George. "The BSCS Special Materials." *The Science Teacher,* 33:54–55, February, 1966.

CHEMISTRY

"ACS Conference Agrees on High School Needs." *Chemical and Engineering News,* 45:48–53, September 11, 1967.

Anderson, Robert H. and Stowe, Donald. "The Curriculum in Chemistry." *School Science and Mathematics: A Report of a Conference for School Administrators,* Kalamazoo, Michigan: Western Michigan University, 1965.

Anderson, William. "Nuffield Chemistry Background Books." *Education in Chemistry,* 3:299–301, November, 1966.

Ashmore, P. G. "On Teaching High School Chemistry." (Book Review) *Science,* 148:1312–1314, June 4, 1965.

Bassow, Herbert. "The CHEM Study Course—An Objective Appraisal." *Science and Math Weekly,* 3:n.p., January 30, 1963.

Baxter, John F. and Young, Jay A. *A Guide to Modern Chemistry, I.* Englewood Cliffs, New Jersey: Prentice-Hall, Inc., 1959.

———. *A Guide to Modern Chemistry, II.* Englewood Cliffs, New Jersey: Prentice-Hall, Inc., 1960.

Baxter, John F. and Steiner, Luke E. *Modern Chemistry, I.* Englewood Cliffs, N. J.: Prentice-Hall, Inc., 1959.

———. *Modern Chemistry, II.* Englewood Cliffs, New Jersey: Prentice-Hall, Inc., 1960.

Bennet, Lloyd M. and Pyke, Barbara Kinnard. "A Discussion of the New Chemistry Programs (CHEMS and CBA) and the Traditional Programs in High School." *School Science and Mathematics,* 66:823–830, December, 1966.

Benson, S. W. "Bond Energies." *Journal of Chemical Education,* 42:502–518, September, 1965.

Bixby, Louis W. "CBA: The Chemical Bond Approach to Chemistry Teaching." *Science and Math Weekly,* 3:1+, April 10, 1963.

Calandra, A. "The New Science Curriculums—A Sharp Dissent." 8:75–82, November, 1964.

Campbell, J. A. "Chemical Education Materials Study." *Journal of Chemical Education,* 38:2–5, January, 1961.

———. "Chemistry: An Experimental Science." *School Review,* 70:51–62, Spring, 1962.

———. "CHEM Study—An Approach to Chemistry Based on Experiments." *New Curricula,* R. W. Heath, editor. New York: Harper and Row, 1964.

———. "CHEM Study: An Experimental Approach to Chemistry." *National Catholic Education Association Bulletin,* 59: 323–324, August, 1962.

Cane, B. S. "School Chemistry: The Search For a New Approach." *Education in Chemistry,* 2:217–226, September, 1965.

Cartmell, E., ed. *New Trends in Chemistry Teaching.* New York: UNESCO, 1967.

"CBA Produces Research-Minded Students." Chemical and Engineering News, 40:38+, March 12, 1962.

"The CBAC Chemistry Course." *Chemistry,* 33:1–29, February, 1960.

"CBAC Evaluation 1960–61." *Chemistry* 35:18–22, September, 1961.

"The CBAC Laboratory Program." *Chemistry,* 34:1–6, April, 1961.

"A CBAC Progress Report." *Chemistry,* 34:1–12, September, 1960.

"Changing Chemistry Curriculum: Symposium." *Journal of Chemical Education,* 43:112–123, March, 1966.

"CHEM Evaluation 1960–61." *Chemistry,* 35:15–17, October, 1961.

"The CHEM Study." *Chemistry,* 34:1–16, January, 1961.

"CHEM Study Course Grows." *Chemistry,* 35:46–47, November, 1962.

"CHEM Study Publishing Final Course Materials." *Chemistry,* 36:42–45, February, 1963.

"CHEM Study Readies for Expanded Trials." *Chemical and Engineering News,* 39:48–50, April 17, 1961.

"CHEM Study Works Toward New High School Course." *Chemical and Engineering News,* 38:50, March 28, 1960.

"Chemical Bonding: A Logical Course." *Chemical and Engineering News,* 37:82, November 30, 1959.

"Chemical Bonds: A Central Theme for High School Chemistry." *Journal of Chemical Education,* 35:57, February, 1958.

"Chemical Education Goes International." *Education in Chemistry,* 4:293+, November, 1967.

Chisman, D. G. "The Nuffield Foundation Science Teaching Project." *Education in Chemistry,* 1:5–6, January, 1964.

Clader, Carl W. "CHEM Study—A Progress Report." *School Science and Mathematics,* 63:377–378, May, 1963.

Colby, E. G. "The New Science Curriculums—A Loud Hurrah." 8:83+, November, 1964.

Cornell, Frederic. "CBA Is Not the Answer." *High Points,* 48:60–62, March, 1966.

Coulson, Ernest H. and Nyholm, R. S. "Aims and Ideas of the Nuffield Chemistry Project." *Education in Chemistry,* 3:229–232, September, 1966.

Craven, Leonard S. "Letters to the Editor." *School Science and Mathematics,* 67:300–301, April, 1967.

Crawley, H. W. "Chemical Bond Approach to the Teaching of Chemistry." *National Catholic Education Association Bulletin,* 59:299–300, August, 1962.

"Exams: The College Boards in Chemistry." *Science,* 147:8, January 1, 1965.

Fast, Kenneth V. "The Role of Laboratory Experiences in the CHEM Study Program." *School Science and Mathematics,* 63:147–156, February, 1963.

"First Examination: The CHEM Study." *Chemistry,* 34:1–9, March, 1961.

Garrett, Alfred B. "The New Chemistry." *The Science Teacher,* 28:15–21, April, 1961.

Geffner, S. L. "Letter to the Editor." *Journal of Chemical Education,* 43:681–682, December, 1966.

Gibboney, Richard A., *et al.* "Curriculum Components and Organization." *Review of Educational Research,* 33:278–292, June, 1963.

Goldberg, Harris P. "An Eclectic View of Current Chemistry Curriculum Studies." *School Science and Mathematics,* 63:770–771, December, 1963.

Groves, Constance. "Nuffield Trials at Canterbury." *Education in Chemistry,* 4:125–126, May, 1967.

Halliwell, H. F. and Van Praagh, G. "The Nuffield Project II: Chemistry 11–16." *The School Science Review,* 48:332–336, June, 1967.

Heath, Robert W. *A Study of Achievement in High School Chem-*

istry. [Reports on both CBA and CHEMS] Princeton: Educational Testing Service, 1962.

———, and Stickell, David W. "CHEM and CBA Effects on Achievement in Chemistry." *The Science Teacher,* 30: 45–46, September, 1963.

Hellman, M. "Teaching of Chemistry: Seminar." *Science,* 133: 1492–1493, May 12, 1961.

"Honors for CBA and CHEM Study." *Chemistry,* 38:5, January, 1965.

"Improvement of High School Chemistry Courses to be Studied Under Science Foundation Grant." *Science,* 131:1087–1088, April 15, 1960.

Jackson, A. "In Defense of Nuffield." *Education in Chemistry,* 4:63–67, March, 1967.

———. "Nuffield Under Trial." *Education in Chemistry,* 3:280–284, November, 1966.

Kelly, Peter. "The Nuffield Science Teaching Project." *The Science Teacher,* 34:26–29, January, 1967.

Kessel, W. G. "The New High School Chemistry Curricula." *Teachers College Journal,* 33:119–122, March, 1962.

Koelsche, C. L. "Quality Science for the Senior High School: The Course in Chemistry." *National Association of Secondary School Principals Bulletin,* 44:111–126, December, 1960.

Lander, A. "Content of the College Preparatory High School Chemistry Course." *Journal of Chemical Education,* 42:231–232, April, 1965.

Lee, Eugene C. "Science Teaching Revitalized." *Texas Outlook,* 46:20–21, February, 1962.

Livermore, A. H. and Ferris, F. C. "Chemical Bond Approach Course in the Classroom," *Science,* 138:1077–1080, December 7, 1962.

———, and Strong, L. E. "Writing Conference for CBA High School Chemistry Project." *Journal of Chemical Education,* 37:209–211, April, 1960.

Maberly, Norman C. "Chemistry Curriculum Patterns in High School." *Science Education,* 51:343–346, October, 1967.

Mathews, J. C. "Nuffield 'O'-Level Chemistry Examinations." *Education in Chemistry,* 4:2–10, January, 1967.

Merrill, R. J. "Chemistry: An Experimental Science." *The Science Teacher,* 30:26–31, April, 1963.

———. "CHEM Study in Action." *Journal of Secondary Education,* 37:69–73, February, 1962.

Miller, Clete L. "Another View of CHEM Study." *The Science Teacher,* 34:60–61, February, 1967.

Monteau, J. R., *et al.* "Evaluation of CBA Chemistry for High School Students." *Science Education,* 47:35–43, February, 1963.

Morlan, Gordon E. "Experiences with the CBA Chemistry Course." *School Science and Mathematics,* 65:425–431, May, 1965.

"New CHEM Films." *Chemistry,* 35:39, April, 1962.

"The New Science Curriculums: Chemistry." *School Management,* 7:58–67, June, 1963.

"Nuffield Project Relates Chemistry to Modern Life." *Chemical and Engineering News,* 45:9–10, September 4, 1967.

"Nuffield Section." *The School Science Review,* 48:841–861, June, 1967.

"Nuffield—The Problem for Schools." *Education in Chemistry,* 3:221, September, 1966.

Organization For European Economic Co-operation. *New Thinking in School Chemistry.* (Report on the OEEC seminar on the status and development of the teaching of school chemistry, Greystones (Ireland), March, 1960), Project STP11, July, 1961.

Owen, J. Randall. "Breakthrough in Chemistry Teaching: High School-College Experiment Tests Chemical Bond Approach." *Overview,* 1:52–53, April, 1960.

Parrish, Clyde. "Teaching High School Chemistry." *California Journal of Secondary Education,* 33:496–501, December, 1958.

Pierce, Edward F. *Modern High School Chemistry, A Recommended Course of Study.* (Science Manpower Project Monographs) New York: Bureau of Publications, Teachers College, Columbia, 1960.

Pode, J. S. F. "CBA and CHEM Study: An Appreciation." *Journal of Chemical Education,* 43:98–103, February, 1966.

———. "Letter to the Editor." *Journal of Chemical Education,* 43:682, December, 1966.

Pye, E. L. and Anderson, K. H. "Test Achievements of Chemistry

Students: Comparison of Achievement of Students in CHEMS, CBA, Conventional, and Other Approaches." *The Science Teacher,* 34:30–32, February, 1967.

Rainey, Robert G. "A Comparison of the CHEM Study Curriculum and a Conventional Approach in Teaching High School Chemistry." *School Science and Mathematics,* 64:539–544, June, 1964.

Ridgway, David W. "CHEM Study Films: Project for Curriculum Improvement." *Educational Screen and Audiovisual Guide,* 41:715–717, December, 1962.

———. "The Success Story of CHEM Study." *Educational Screen and Audiovisual Guide,* 46:23–25, October, 1967.

Salstrom, David and Eppenschied, James. "An Experimental Use of the CHEM Study Program." *Ideas Educational,* n.v.:9–18, 1964.

Seaborg, G. T. "New Currents in Chemical Education." *Chemical and Engineering News,* 38:97+, October 17, 1960.

Silber, Robert L. "Chemical Education Materials Study Approach to Introductory Chemistry." *School Science and Mathematics,* 61:114–118, February, 1961.

———. "New Curriculum Patterns for Chemistry Teachers." *The American Association of Colleges for Teacher Education Fiftieth Yearbook.* Washington, D. C.: Amer. Assoc. of Col. for Teach. Ed., 1962. Pp. 121–127.

Strong, L. E. "Chemistry as a Science in the High School." *School Review,* 70:44–50, Spring, 1962.

———. "College Chemistry: The Road to Nonsense or Science." *Chemical and Engineering News,* 43:124–132, February 22, 1965.

———. "Facts, Students, Ideas." *Journal of Chemical Education,* 39:126–129, March, 1962.

———. "Insight in Chemistry for the Average Student." *The Science Teacher,* 34:60, February, 1967.

———, and Pimental, George. "Greetings from CBA and CHEM Study." *Chemistry,* 37:24–25, January, 1964.

———, and Wilson, M. K. "Chemical Bonds: A Central Theme for High School Chemistry." *Journal of Chemical Education,* 35:56–58, February, 1958.

Tremlett, R. "The Nuffield Foundation Science Teaching Project

IV: Apparatus and Laboratory Organization—Chemistry." *The School Science Review,* 48:663–674, June, 1967.

Uricheck, Michael J. "Research Proposal: An Attempt to Evaluate the Success of the CBA and CHEM Study Chemistry Courses." *Science Education,* 51:5–11, February, 1967.

Walker, Noojin. "Chem Study, CBA, and Modern Chemistry: A Comparison." *School Science and Mathematics,* 67:603–609, October, 1967.

Walter, Robert I. "Changing Curriculum in Chemistry: Some Contemporary Developments: Report of a Survey." *Journal of Chemical Education,* 42:524–528, October, 1965.

Westmeyer, P. "Chemical Bond Approach to Introductory Chemistry." *School Science and Mathematics,* 61:317–322, May, 1961.

———. "Twentieth Century Mythology." *High School Journal,* 46:244–247, April, 1963.

EARTH SCIENCE

Beebe, B. Warren. "The Potential of ESCP." (Editorial) *Geotimes,* 12:9, December, 1967.

Bisque, Ramon E. "Investigating the Earth." *Geotimes,* 10:14–17, February, 1966.

Boyer, Robert E. and Snyder, John L. "Teachers of Earth Science." *Geotimes,* 8:13–16, March, 1964.

Cloud, Preston E., Jr. "Earth Science Today." *Science,* 144:1428–1431, June 19, 1964.

Coash, John R. "Earth Science in the Secondary Schools." *Geotimes,* 7:26–29, March, 1963.

Conselman, Frank B. "ESCP Textbook." (Book Review) *Geotimes,* 12:34–36, September, 1967.

Dorr, Ann Pierce. "ESCP Textbook." (Book Review) *Geotimes,* 12:36+, September, 1967.

"Earth Science Course Develops Physical Geography." *High School Geography Project Newsletter,* No. 12, March, 1967.

"Earth Science Curriculum Gains Momentum." *The Prentice-Hall Science Newsletter,* No. 16, pp. 1+, Spring, 1964.

"Earth Science Curriculum Project." *Geotimes,* 8:14–19, July-August, 1963.

"ESCP 1965." *Geotimes,* 10:16–17, October, 1965.

Ferris, Frederick L. "The Princeton Junior High School Science Project." *Journal of Research in Science Teaching,* 1:281–284, No. 3, 1963.

Gatewood, Claude E. "Impact Ahead." *Geotimes,* 7:8–12, January-February, 1963.

"Geostudy Questionnaire." *Geotimes,* 10:14–15, October, 1965.

Heller, Robert L. "The Earth Science Curriculum Project." *Journal of Geological Education,* 12:64–68, June, 1964.

———. "The Earth Science Curriculum Project." *Journal of Research in Science Teaching,* 1:272–275, No. 3, 1963.

———. "The Earth Science Curriculum Project—A Report of Progress." *Journal of Research in Science Teaching,* 2:330–334, No. 4, 1964.

———. "The Secondary School Earth Science Course in Science Education." *Journal of Geological Education,* 13:71–74, June, 1965.

Hook, John C. "New Programs in Earth Science." *Teachers College Journal,* 33:122–125, March, 1962.

Hubbard, T. N. "Earth Science Now in Orbit." *American School Board Journal,* 151:26–27, July, 1965.

"In the Societies." *Geotimes,* 9:25, March, 1965.

Jones, Daniel J. "The Curriculum in Earth Science." *School Science and Mathematics: A Report of a Conference for School Administrators,* Kalamazoo, Michigan: Western Michigan University, 1965.

Kosoloski, John E. "The Pennsylvania Earth and Space Science Program." *Geotimes,* 7:15–16, October, 1962.

Ladd, George T. "ESCP . . . An Investigative Approach For Teaching Earth Science to Students of All Levels of Ability." *Journal of Geological Education,* 16:61–64, April, 1968.

Laux, Dean M. "Earth Science Courses in New Jersey and the Qualifications of Teachers." *Geotimes,* 7:17–19, October, 1962.

Lewis, Richard S. "ESCP Moves Ahead." *Geotimes,* 9:16–18, September, 1964.

Lokke, Donald H. "Objectives of Pre-College Geological Education." *Geotimes,* 7:18–20, November-December, 1962.

Mac Mahan, Horace, Jr. "Princeton Project or ESCP: A Difficult Choice." *School Science and Mathematics,* 66:86–91, January, 1966.

Matthews, William H., III. "Current Status of Earth Science in Secondary Schools." *Journal of Geological Education,* 12:60–63, June, 1964.

———. "Earth Science In Secondary Schools." *Geotimes,* 13:14–16, March, 1968.

———. "Growth of Earth Science in Secondary Schools." *School Science and Mathematics,* 63:637–646, November, 1963.

Merrill, William M. and Shrum, John W. "Planning for Earth Science Teacher Preparation." *Journal of Geological Education,* 14:23–25, February, 1966.

———, *et al.* "Recommendations: Academic Preparation of Secondary School Earth Science Teachers." *Journal of Geological Education,* 14:29–32, February, 1966.

Moss, John H. "The Teacher Problem in High School Earth Science Courses." *Journal of Geological Education,* 10:41–44, June, 1962.

Pollinger, D. L. and Syrewicz, E. R. "Earth Science." *School and Community,* 53:17, November, 1966.

Renaud, Jane W. "Time, Space and Matter." *Geotimes,* 12:19, April, 1967.

Roy, Chalmer J. "Let's Teach Geology as the Science of the Earth." *Journal of Geological Education,* 14:47–50, April, 1966.

Samples, Robert E. "Death of an Investigation." *Journal of Geological Education,* 14:69–72, April, 1966.

Shea, James H. "Earth Science Curriculum Project: A Progress Report." *The Science Teacher,* 32:43+, February, 1965.

———. "Highlights of 1965 ESCP Survey of Earth Science Teachers." *Journal of Geological Education,* 14:9–12, February, 1966.

Shourd, Malvin L. "Earth Science-Choice for Junior High School." *The Science Teacher,* 30:53+, November, 1963.

Shrum, John W. "Recommendations for a Basic Academic Preparation for Earth Science Teachers." *Journal of Geological Education,* 14:26–28, February, 1966.

Snyder, John. "A Look at the Current Status of AGI Educational Programs." *Geotimes,* 7:32–33, April, 1963.

Stephenson, Robert C. "Earth Science Curriculum Project." *The Science Teacher,* 31:21–23, March, 1964.

———. "New Curriculum in Earth Sciences." *School Life,* 45:24–26, October, 1962.

———. "Teacher-Training Problems in Earth Science." *Journal of Geological Education,* 12:74–78, June, 1964.

Stone, Donald B. "Growth of Earth Science in New York State." *Geotimes,* 7:13–14, October, 1962.

Taylor, Peter. "A New Science Course for Junior High School." *Journal of Geological Education,* 11:135–137, December, 1963.

Willard, Gates. "Importance of Earth Sciences in the Curriculum." *The Science Teacher,* 28:22+, April, 1961.

Winchell, Vaughn F. "ESCP Textbook." (In Letters to the Editor) *Geotimes,* 13:6–8, January, 1968.

ENGINEERING CONCEPTS CURRICULUM PROJECT

Commission on Engineering Education. *Engineering Concepts Curriculum Project.* Washington, D. C.: Com. on Eng. Ed., n.d.

Commission on Engineering Education. *A Summer Study Report of the Engineering Concepts Curriculum Project,* Report No. 1. Washington, D. C.: Com. on Eng. Ed., 1964.

Commission on Engineering Education. *Working Papers of the Summer Study Report of the Engineering Concepts Curriculum Project,* Report No. 2. Washington, D. C.: Com. on Eng. Ed., 1964.

David, E. E., Jr. "A Role for Engineering and Technology in School Education." *The Science Teacher,* 32:17, March, 1965.

———, and Truxal, J. G. " 'The Man-Made World,' A New Course for High Schools." *Science,* 156:914–920, May 19, 1967.

"ECCP Second Trial is Under Way." *The Physics Teacher,* 5:72, February, 1967.

"Engineering Concepts Curriculum Project." *The Physics Teacher,* 6:114, March, 1968.

PHYSICAL SCIENCE

Beaird, Robert W. "The Introductory Physical Science Course in Junior High." *School Science and Mathematics.* 67:7:624–630, October, 1967.

Diazgranados, Frederick A. "IPS in Uruguay." *The Science Teacher,* 35:1:53, January, 1967.

Dillon, Thomas J. "Teacher's Role Redefined In New Science Course." *Educational Equipment and Materials.* Fall, 1966, p. 17–19.

Smith, M. K. and Cross, Judson B. *Introductory Physical Science: A Progress Report.* Watertown, Mass.: Educational Services Incorporated. (no date). The following series of articles on IPS are included in this report:

"Objectives and Content of the IPS Course." Uri Haber-Schaim

"The First Trial of the Course at Concord-Carlisle High School." Thomas J. Dillon

"Introductory Physical Science and the Average Student." John H. Dodge

"Introductory Physical Science in a Ninth to Twelfth-Grade School." Edward A. Shore

"Introductory Physical Science as a Terminal Course." James A. Walter

"Relationship of the IPS Course to the New Chemistry Curricula." M. Kent Wilson

"IPS and the New Biological Sciences Curriculum." Claude Welch

"Feedback: Its Form and Function." Nancy Nelson

"IPS Achievement Tests." Raymond E. Thompson

PHYSICS

Arons, Arnold. "The New High School Physics Course." *Physics Today,* 13:20–25, June, 1960.

Baker, J. R. "How Can Teachers Keep Up to Date." *Physics Education,* 1:241–246, November, 1966.

Beatty, H. Russell. "Implications of the PSSC for Technical Institutes." *Harvard Educational Review,* 29:23–25, Winter, 1959.

Black, H. T. "PSSC In Indiana." *Teachers College Journal,* 33:127–129, March, 1962.

Boulay, Peter. "Good Enough for Galileo." *American Education,* 4:15–18, December, 1967–January, 1968.

Brakken, E. "Intellectual Factors in PSSC and Conventional High

School Physics." *Journal of Research in Science Teaching,* 3:19–25, No. 1, 1965.

Brauer, O. L. "Attempts to Improve High School Physics Education." *Science Education,* 47:372–376, October, 1963.

———. "Something Dangerously New In Physics Teaching." *Science Education,* 47:365–372, October, 1963.

———. "Conventional Physics Against PSSC Physics." *Science Education,* 49:170–171, March, 1965.

"Bringing Physics Closer to Cultural Life." *Phi Delta Kappan,* 48:148, December, 1962.

"British Curriculum Revision." *Physics Today,* 18:80, July, 1965.

Calandra, Alexander. "New Science Curriculums—A Sharp Dissent." *School Management,* 8:76–82, November, 1964.

———. "Some Observations of the Work of the PSSC." *Harvard Educational Review,* 29:19–27, Winter, 1959.

Cheldelin, Vernon H. and Fiasca, Michael. "A Synthesis of the New Curricula in Physics and Chemistry for the Secondary School." *Journal of Research in Science Teaching,* 2:283–287, 1964.

Colby, Edward. "The New Science Curriculums—A Loud Hurrah." *School Management,* 8:83+, November, 1964.

Craven, Leonard S. "How Many Take PSSC?" (In Letters to the Editor) *Physics Today,* 20:9, June, 1967.

Creutz, Edward. "AIP Corporate Associates Study Physics and Society." *Physics Today,* 20:63–64, November, 1967.

Crumb, Glenn H. "Understanding of Science in High School Physics." *Journal of Research in Science Teaching,* 3:246–250, No. 3, 1965.

Dartnell, W. W. "In Defense of PSSC." (In Letters to the Editor). *The Physics Teacher,* 3:371, November, 1965.

David, Edward E., Jr. "Engineering Concepts." *Physics Today,* 20:34+, March, 1967.

———, and Truxal, J. G. "The Man-Made World: A New Course for High Schools." *Science,* 55:914–920, May, 1967.

"Declining Physics Enrollment." *Science,* 155:984, February 24, 1967.

Derby, S. K. and Campbell, Donald. "The PSSC Curriculum in Physics." *School Science and Mathematics: A Report of a Conference for School Administrators.* Kalamazoo, Michigan: Western Michigan University, 1965. pp. 37–40.

Detenbeck, R. W. and DiLavore, P. "Harvard Project Physics." *The Physics Teacher,* 5:233, May, 1967.

Drozin, V. G. "Need for Multiplicity of Physics Courses." *The Physics Teacher,* 3:371, November, 1965.

———. "What Should Be Done to Increase the Enrollment in Physics." *The Physics Teacher,* 4:23+, January, 1966.

Easley, J. A., Jr. "The Physical Science Study Committee and Educational Theory." *The Harvard Educational Review,* 29:4–11, Winter, 1959.

Ellis, R. Hobart, Jr. "Is Physics Too Tough?" (Editorial) *Physics Today,* 19:152, April, 1966.

Ferris, Frederick L., Jr. "An Achievement Test Report," *The Science Teacher,* 26:576–579, December, 1959.

———. "The Physical Science Study—Will it Succeed?" *Harvard Educational Review,* 29:29–32, Winter, 1959.

———. "Testing for Physics Achievement." *American Journal of Physics,* 28:269–278, March, 1960.

———. "Testing in the New Curriculum: Numerology, 'Tyranny' or Common Sense." *The School Review,* 70:112–131, Spring, 1962.

———, and Lane, Doris A. "Test Year for New Physics Course." *College Board Review,* n.v.:26–28, No. 36, 1958.

Finger, John A., Jr., Dillon, John A., Jr., and Corbin, Frederic. "Performance in Introductory College Physics and Previous Instruction in Physics." *Journal of Research in Science Teaching,* 3:61–65, No. 1, 1965.

Finlay, Gilbert C. "Physical Science Study Committee." *School Review,* 70:63–81, Spring, 1962.

———. "Physical Science Study Committee: A Status Report." *The Science Teacher,* 26:574–576, December, 1959.

———. "Physical Science Study Committee: Summary of Judgments Made by Teachers." *The Science Teacher,* 26:579–581, December, 1959.

———. "The Physical Science Study: What are the Questions?" *The Science Teacher,* 24:327–329, November, 1957.

———. "Secondary School Physics: The Physical Science Study Committee." *American Journal of Physics,* 28:286–293, March, 1960.

Friedman, Francis L. "The Physical Science Study: A Blueprint." *The Science Teacher,* 24:320–323, November, 1957.

Frymier, Jack. "Redirections: The Person In the Process." *The California Journal for Instructional Improvement,* 2:2–19, March, 1968.

Gibboney, Richard A., *et al.* "Curriculum Components and Organization: Physics." *Review of Educational Research,* 33:278–292, June, 1963.

Haber-Schaim, Uri. "The Physical Science Study Committee: The Working Session on Physics Teaching at the Cavandish Laboratory, Cambridge." *Contemporary Physics,* 3:368–374, June, 1962.

———. "The PSSC Course." *Physics Today,* 20:26+, March, 1967.

———. "The Use of the PSSC Physics Course in the United States." *The Physics Teacher,* 6:66–67, February, 1968.

Harris, John. "The Laboratory and Project Physics." *The Physics Teacher,* 5:224–229, May, 1967.

———, and Ahlgren, A. "Apparatus—Lecture Demonstration and Laboratory. Classroom Technique." *The Physics Teacher,* 4:314–322, October, 1966.

Heath, Robert W. "Comparison of Achievement in Two Physics Courses." *Journal of Experimental Education,* 32:347–354, Summer, 1964.

"High-School Physics to Get Help." *Physics Today,* 18:101–102, November, 1965.

Hipsher, Warren L. "Study of High School Physics Achievement." *The Science Teacher,* 28:36–37, October, 1961.

Holton, Gerald. "Harvard Project Physics." *Physics Today,* 20:31+, March, 1967.

———. "Project Physics: A Report on Its Aims and Current Status." *The Physics Teacher,* 5:198–211, May, 1967.

Huntsinger, Vance L. "High School Learning." (In Letters to the Editor) *Physics Today,* 20:13, March, 1967.

Hurd, Paul DeH. "The New Curriculum Movement in Science." *The Science Teacher,* 29:7–9, February, 1962.

John, R. T. "Use of PSSC Physics in Minor Seminaries." *National Catholic Education Association Bulletin,* 58:75, August, 1961.

Kaufman, Clinton. "High School Physics Enrollment." *The Physics Teacher,* 3:120, March, 1965.

Kerr, John F. "Science Teaching and Social Change." *The School Science Review,* 48:301–308, June, 1967.

Killian, James R., Jr. "New Goals for Science and Engineering."

Education: An Instrument of National Goals, Paul Hanna, editor. New York: McGraw-Hill, 1962.

Kimball, Merritt E. "Student Opinion Changes During a Year of Studying the Harvard Project Physics Course." *Journal of Research in Science Teaching,* 4:173–174, 1966.

King, Allen L. "Decline of Percentage Enrollment in High School Physics." *The Physics Teacher,* 3:119–120, March, 1965.

Kleinman, Gladys S. "All is Not Lost: The High School Physics Enrollment Picture is Not as Black as it Seems!" *The Physics Teacher,* 3:120–121, March, 1965.

Klopfer, Leo E. "The Physics Course of the Physical Science Study Committee—A View from the Classroom." *Harvard Educational Review,* 29:26–28, Winter, 1959.

Knauss, H. P. "Physics For Secondary Schools." *American Journal of Physics,* 26:378–380, September, 1958.

Koerner, James D. "EDC: General Motors of Curriculum Reform." *Saturday Review,* 50:56+, August 19, 1967.

———. "Reform and Revolution in English Education." *Saturday Review,* 50:61–63, January 21, 1967.

Kraus, Alfred A., Jr. "Letters." *Physics Today,* 20:13+, March, 1967.

Lessinger, Leon M. "Evaluation of PSSC Physics." *Journal of Secondary Education,* 37:97–99, February, 1962.

"Letters-to-the-Editor." *The Physics Teacher,* 3:271–273, September, 1965.

Lindahl, Goran. "PSSC in Sweden." (In Letters to the Editor) *The Physics Teacher,* 4:279–280, September, 1966.

Little, E. P. "A Commentary." *Harvard Educational Review,* 29:33–36, Winter, 1959.

———. "New Emphasis on the 'How' of Physics." *Nation's Schools,* 65:104–105, February, 1960.

———. "The Physical Science Study: From These Beginnings." *The Science Teacher,* 24:316–319, November, 1957.

———. "PSSC: A Physics Program." *Educational Leadership,* 17:167+, December, 1959.

———, *et al.* "A Symposium: The Physical Science Study Committee." *Harvard Education Reviews,* 29:1–3, Winter, 1959.

Little, Noel C., Ford, Everett J. and Paldy, Lester G. "Book and Film Reviews." *The Physics Teacher,* 4:88–93, February, 1966.

Maddox, J. "The Nuffield Physics Project." *Physics Education,* 1:3–7, May, 1966.

Marsh, Paul E. "Wellsprings of Strategy: Considerations Affecting Innovations by the PSSC." *Innovation in Education,* Matthew B. Miles, editor. New York: Bureau of Publications Teachers College, Columbia University, 1964.

———, and Gortner, Ross A. *Federal Aid to Science Education:* Two Programs. Syracuse, New York: Syracuse University Press, 1963.

Marshall, J. Stanley. "Evolving Science Education in Florida." *The Science Teacher,* 29:27, December, 1962.

Martin, Henry C. "Comments Regarding Our Low Physics Enrollment." *The Physics Teacher,* 3:118, March, 1965.

Matthews, Richard E. "PSSC and the Low Ability Student." *The Physics Teacher,* 5:34–35, January, 1967.

Meyes, E. "Pros and Cons of the Physical Science Study Committee Curriculum." *National Catholic Education Association Bulletin,* 57:294–295, August, 1960.

Michels, Walter C. "The Teaching of Elementary Physics." *Scientific American,* 198:56–62+, April, 1958.

"New Physics Class." *Time,* 71:40–41, March 17, 1958.

"The 'New' Science Curriculum." *School Management,* 7:58–67, June, 1963.

Newton, David E. "A New Look at Physics: Harvard Project Physics." *Michigan Science Teachers Bulletin,* 14:7–9, September, 1966.

The Nuffield Foundation Science Teaching Project. n.loc.: Longmans/Penguin Books, October, 1964.

O.E.C.D. *Teaching Physics Today.* Switzerland: O.E.C.D. Publications, 1965.

O.E.E.C. "The Teaching of Physics in Schools." *Physics Today,* 14:30–37, January, 1961.

"Physical Science Study Committee: A Planning Conference Report." *Physics Today,* 10:28–29, March, 1957.

"The Physical Science Study Committee Program in Physics." *Welch Physics and Chemistry Digest,* 11:8–9, No. 3, 1961.

"Physics Education Crisis Revealed by American Institute of Physics Study." *Welch Physics and Chemistry Digest,* 15:14–16, No. 1, 1965.

Physics In Your High School. (Prepared by American Institute of

Physics) New York: McGraw-Hill Book Company, Inc., 1960.

Poorman, Lawrence G. "Indiana Physics Teachers React to PSSC." *Science Education,* 49:171–172, March, 1965.

Potter, J. G. "Comments on Results of the Physics Teacher Survey." *The Physics Teacher,* 3:118–119, March, 1965.

"Proceedings of the Ad Hoc Advisory Conference on Secondary School Physics." *Welch Physics and Chemistry Digest,* 16:5–11, No. 1, 1966.

"Project Physics." *American Institute of Physics Educational Newsletter,* 7:n.pp., September 16, 1964.

"Project Physics: Final Test." (Physical Science Notes) *Science News,* 92:12, January 6, 1968.

"Project Physics." *Physics Today,* 17:98, September, 1964.

"PSSC Versus Conventional Physics." *The Science Teacher,* 29: 47+, February, 1962.

Rathe, Dale D. "Certain Physics Generalizations Desirable for Students to Attain Before Taking the Physical Science Study Committee's High School Physics Course." *Science Education,* 49:127–138, March, 1965.

"Razors at the Frontier; M.I.T. Program on Teaching High School Physics." *Time,* 70:38+, July 29, 1957.

"Review of the Nuffield Books." *Physics Education,* 2:292–294, September, 1967.

"Revolt Against Physics?" (New York Times editorial, February, 12, 1968) in "A Point of View." *Science,* 159:1085, March 8, 1968.

Ritchie, W. R. "Physics in the Scottish Schools." *The Physics Teacher,* 4:63–67, February, 1966.

Rogers, Eric M. "The Nuffield Project." *Physics Today,* 20:40+, March, 1967.

Rutherford, F. James. "Flexibility and Variety in Physics." *The Physics Teacher,* 5:215–221, May, 1967.

———, and Welch, Wayne W. "Evaluation Activities of Harvard Project Physics." *Science Education News,* American Association for the Advancement of Science Publication No. 67–7, pp. 5–6, June, 1967.

Sawyer, Ralph A. "Reflections on the High School Curriculum." *School Science and Mathematics,* 65:389–400, May, 1965.

Schrag, Philip G. and Holland, James G. "Programming Motion Pictures: The conversion of a PSSC film into a Program." *AV Communication Review,* 13:418–422, Winter, 1965.

Smith, Daniel M., Schagrin, Morton L., and Poorman, Eugene L. "The Multi-Media System Study of Harvard Project Physics." *School Science and Mathematics,* 68:95–102, February, 1968.

Smith, George F. "PSSC Applied Physics." *The Physics Teacher,* 3:312–318, October, 1965.

"Softer Physics Teaching." *Science News,* 91:27, January 7, 1967.

Stepan, O. M. and Osborne, J. M. "The Nuffield Foundation Science Teaching Project V: Physics Apparatus and Laboratory Design." *The School Science Review,* 48:676–684, June, 1967.

Straley, Joseph W. "Science Curricula in Transition." (Editorial) *Physics Teacher,* 1:76–77, May, 1963.

"A Technologist's Views on Present Trends in Physics Education." *Education in Science,* n.v.:22–24, February, 1966.

"A Third Course," (Editorial) *The Physics Teacher,* 3:169, April, 1965.

Trent, John. "The Attainment of the Concept 'Understanding Science,' Using Contrasting Physics Courses." *Journal of Research in Science Teaching,* 3:224–229, 1965.

Trowbridge, Leslie W. "A Comparison of the Objectives and Instruction Materials in Two Types of High School Physics Courses." *Science Education,* 49:117–122, March, 1965.

———. "Comparison of the Objectives of Traditional High School Physics With the Objectives of the Physical Science Study Committee Course, and an Analysis of the Instructional Materials of the Physical Science Study Committee Course." Ann Arbor: University of Michigan, 1961, in *Dissertation Abstracts,* 22:812, 1961.

UNESCO. "Harvard Project Physics." *New Trends in Physics Teaching, I.* France: UNESCO, 1968, Pp. 132–136.

———. "Science Course Improvement Projects." *New Trends in Physics Teaching, I.* France: UNESCO, 1968. Pp. 122–126.

Vitrogan, David. *Modern High School Physics: A Recommended Course of Study.* Science Manpower Project Monographs. New York: Bureau of Publications, Teachers College, Columbia University, 1959.

Walsh, John. "Education Reform: British Reorganize Secondary Schools." *Science,* 159:68–70, January 5, 1968.

Walton, Harold F. "The Humanistic Values of Science." *Chemistry,* 38:8–13, December, 1965.

Waterman, Alan T. "The Education and Training of Physicists." (Editorial) *Physics Today,* 20:144, November, 1967.

Watson, Fletcher G. "Comments on the Program of the Physical Science Study Committee." *Harvard Educational Review,* 29:12–15, Winter, 1959.

———, "Why Do We Need More Physics Courses?" *The Physics Teacher,* 5:212–214, May, 1967.

Welch, Wayne W. "High School Physics Enrollments." (In Letters to the Editor) *Physics Today,* 20:9+, September, 1967.

———. "The Impact of National Curriculum Projects—The Need for Accurate Assessment." *School Science and Mathematics,* 68:225–234, March, 1968.

———. "The Need for Evaluating National Curriculum Projects." *Phi Delta Kappan,* 44:530–532, May, 1968.

———, and Walberg, Herbert J. "A Design for Curriculum Evaluation." *Science Education,* 52:10–16, February, 1968.

Wenham, E. J. "The Nuffield Foundation Science Teaching Project-III: Physics 11–16. *The School Science Review,* 48:337–346, March, 1967.

"What are the New Curriculums?" *School Management,* 5:90–92, September, 1960.

White, Stephen, "The Physical Science Study Committee: The Planning and Structure of the Course." *Contemporary Physics,* 2:39–54, October, 1960.

———, and Welch, Wayne W. "Achievement Testing Program of Project Physics." *The Physics Teacher,* 5:229–231, May, 1967.

Williams, Van Zandt. "Pre-College Physics." (Editorial) *The Physics Teacher,* 4:75–76, February, 1966.

Wray, John H. "Physics In Central America." *Physics Today,* 20:43–52, January, 1967.

Wyatt, H. V. "Science Teaching After Nuffield." *University Quarterly,* 20:289–295, June, 1966.

Young, Victor J. "A Report on Pre-College Physics." *The Physics Teacher,* 4:20–22, January, 1966.

———. "Survey on Enrollment in Physics." *The Physics Teacher,* 3:117, March, 1965.

Zacharias, Jerrold R. "The Physical Science Study: Into the Laboratory." *The Science Teacher,* 24:324–326, November, 1957.

———. "Team Approach to Education." *American Journal of Physics,* 29:347–349, June, 1961.

———, and White, Stephen. "Requirements for Major Curriculum Revision." *School and Society,* 92:66–72, February 22, 1964.

Index

PRINTED IN U.S.A.